MATHS 9420 1960 -I

INFORMATION AND
DECISION PROCESSES

LIST OF CONTRIBUTORS

GEORGE W. BROWN, *Director of Western Data Processing Center, and Professor of Business Administration, University of California at Los Angeles*

HERMAN CHERNOFF, *Professor of Statistics, Stanford University*

J. L. DOOB, *Professor of Mathematics, University of Illinois*

MERRILL M. FLOOD, *Professor of Industrial Engineering, University of Michigan*

WASSILY HOFFDING, *Professor of Mathematics, University of North Carolina*

DAVID ROSENBLATT, *Research Consultant, Washington, D. C.*

MURRAY ROSENBLATT, *Professor of Applied Mathematics, Brown University*

CLAUDE SHANNON, *Professor of Mathematics, and Electrical Engineering, Massachusetts Institute of Technology*

MILTON SOBEL, *Bell Telephone Laboratories, Allentown, Pennsylvania*

PATRICK SUPPES, *Professor of Philosophy, Stanford University*

LIONEL WEISS, *Associate Professor of Mechanical Engineering, Cornell University*

JACOB WOLFOWITZ, *Professor of Mathematics, Cornell University*

INFORMATION AND DECISION PROCESSES

EDITED BY

ROBERT E. MACHOL
Purdue University

McGRAW-HILL BOOK COMPANY, INC.

New York   Toronto   London

1960

INFORMATION AND DECISION PROCESSES

PREFACE

In April of 1959 a Symposium on Information and Decision Processes was held at Purdue University. The conference lasted two and one half days, each of the ten speakers being allotted half of a morning or afternoon. This book is an outgrowth of that conference, in that each speaker has contributed a chapter; some of these chapters are identical to the conference presentations, while in other cases the authors have chosen to modify their papers, or to submit altogether different papers, more suitable for a book of this nature. In addition, two of the outstanding papers from the 1958 Purdue Conference on the same subject are included.

I wish to take this opportunity to thank the authors for their speedy action (in most cases) in submitting their manuscripts, and for their cooperative attitude (in all cases) toward the wearying trivialities of my editorship. I also wish to acknowledge the outstanding co-chairmanship of Professors Paul Randolph and Judah Rosenblatt who arranged and managed the conference. The typists, Loree Lentz and Lisa Rosenblatt, deserve thanks for the care, above and beyond the call of duty, which they lavished on the manuscript. And my wife, Florence, has my special appreciation for encouraging me to take on this task although it meant much extra time alone for her.

Robert E. Machol

February, 1960

TABLE OF CONTENTS

INTRODUCTION

In April of 1959, ten of this country's leading scholars forgathered on the campus of Purdue University to discuss the nature of information and the nature of decision. Their contributions toward these questions appear in this book. What thread ties together these contributions? What interests do these men have in common? For what reason did they travel collectively so many thousands of miles to come to this conference?

To answer these questions it is necessary to view the changing aspect of the scientific approach to epistemology, and the striking progress which has been wrought in the very recent past. The decade from 1940 to 1950 witnessed the operation of the first stored-program digital computer. The concept of information was quantified, and mathematical theories were developed for communication (Shannon) and decision (Wald). Known mathematical techniques were applied to new and important fields, as the techniques of complex-variable theory to the analysis of feedback systems and the techniques of matrix theory to the analysis of systems under multiple linear constraints. The word "cybernetics" was coined, and with it came the realization of the many analogies between control and communication in men and in automata. New terms like "operations research" and "system engineering" were introduced; despite their occasional use by charlatans, they have signified enormous progress in the solution of exceedingly complex problems, through the application of quantitativeness and objectivity.

At this time it is difficult to put one's finger on any single contribution in the decade 1950 - 1960 which is comparable to those above, and yet progress has probably been even greater. From the point of view of an educator, one cannot overlook the wide distribution which has been given to these ideas. There has been remarkable progress from analysis to synthesis, always a sign of maturity in a field of analytic endeavour. There has been consolidation, for example in the establishment of a more rigorous basis for information theory; there has been unification, for example in the demonstration of the formal similarity between game theory and linear programming; there has been application to mathematically more difficult situations, for example nonlinear servo systems and information channels with memory; there has been implementation, as in commercially available computers which by any reasonable measure are hundreds of times more powerful than the primitive devices of 1950; there has been delimitation of the boundaries of many of these fields.

Yet more significant than any of the above is the enlargement of view - point which has taken place. It is difficult to change one's frame of reference, and so one does not realize how great are the changes which have taken place in this decade. There has been a startling enlargement of the areas which we are now willing to discuss scientifically, to include subjects which would have been rejected a few years ago as sheer metaphysics. Equally startling is the enlargement in predictions -- reputable computer engineers now confidently predict achievements for their machines which would have been defined a few years ago as "thinking", and therefore by definition unattainable by machines.

In fact it is these very questions -- within these new areas and subject to these new predictions of achievement -- which are the subject matter of the present book. Because we have discovered in this past decade that thinking, and decision, are not solely the province of the metaphysicist, but are appropriate subjects for scientific inquiry. They have been rendered so, to a considerable extent, by the very authors of this volume. It is no coincidence that of these twelve authors, nine are professional mathematicians, and the other three (an economist, a philosopher, and an electrical engineer) are well known as competent mathematicians. For it is primarily by means of mathematical techniques that these subjects have been brought to the stage where objective, quantitative, scientific methodology can be applied to them. Out of that methodology will inexorably come the applications and the understanding which are the twin goals sought, one or the other, by all the many scholars, be they engineers or scientists, who are working so assiduously in this field.

Wiener has wisely reviewed the old mechanist - vitalist controversy in this new context, and asserted that it had been relegated to the limbo of badly posed questions. But it would seem that we have revived this controversy. And we have revived it with a bald mechanist affirmation which would have brought us all to the pyre a few centuries back. We assert that it is possible to describe analytically any human function which can be reasonably defined in objective terms -- and we specifically include in such

functions "thinking" insofar as that term is definable. If by "thinking" one means be-

ing able to do arithmetic, or play a good game of chess, or learn from experience, or

make optimal decisions in exceedingly complex situations, then we assert that thinking

can be described analytically. And there are two important corollaries: if it can be

described analytically, it can be simulated; and if it can be simulated, it can be per-

formed mechanically.

Two caveats are needed. Of course we cannot do all these things today -- but we

assert today that these things are achievable in the foreseeable future, and we are

bent on approaching them. As the space engineer today is confident that he can and

will put a living man on the surface of Mars within a few years, although he cannot

say just how or when, so are we confident that we shall build chess-playing machines,

and decision-making machines, and near-optimal communication systems. And this

is an advance; such an assertion would have been dismissed as wild and unscientific

a few years ago, as would a prediction of imminent interplanetary travel.

The second caveat concerns delimitation of our field of competence, and therefore

of our field of interest. We are not concerned with those functions which are charac-

teristic of emotion rather than thought. He would be a fool who would assert today

that love is purely a matter of biochemistry -- although he would also be a fool who

would assert that biochemistry has nothing to do with it.

An example is my own research interest which centers around the construction of

mathematical models of the teaching process. I have not thus far achieved significant

results, but I am convinced not only that I can do so, but that it will be easy. From

models of this sort it is then hoped that one can go on to the far more difficult, but far

more useful, task of constructing mathematical models of the learning process. Such

a research project is made possible in part by modern tools (notably the large digital

computer), but also in part by viewpoint. It is a truism to say that a proper statement

of the problem is a long step towards its solution. What we have done in the past de-

cade is to restate our basic problem, and to state it in a form which makes a solution

look feasible.

This basic problem is that of building a mathematical model of thought processes,

and in particular of those aspects of thought which are concerned with information and decision processes. The perceptron is one type of model -- a set of memory devices connected in random fashion -- which has not yet achieved useful results but certainly seems to be a promising approach. The self - adaptive feedback control system -- which goes beyond the normal servo function of controlling its output, and in addition controls the parameters by which it controls its output -- is another which has already achieved pragmatic results in equipment control. It may be that the question of self-adaptation is a key to the whole question of how the human functions in a decisioning situation. For in many cases the ability of the human mind to adapt itself to a changing and complex environment is beyond our present aims in model construction.

On the other hand, we have many models which are already an improvement on human capabilities. We assert apodictically that in a transportation situation which is describable by the familiar linear model, a mathematician with a computer can always do at least as well, and usually better, than an experienced man operating purely on intuition. Such models lead to brute-force solutions of many interesting problems, which the human brain does not solve by brute-force methods. As George Brown warns us in an article in this book, we must not place our reliance exclusively on brute-force methods, but must also attempt to simulate the gestalt approach which the human uses, and which he uses on so many problems with a not inconsiderable degree of success.

Consider the diagram shown here. If one were asked to pick the point corresponding to the center of gravity, he would have little difficulty in choosing a point which was approximately correct, and in being reasonably confident  that this point was, in fact, approximately correct. On the other hand, he might have considerable difficulty explaining just how he had arrived at his choice, or why he was confident that it was close to the correct center of gravity. At the present state of advance, it would not be possible to program a computer to take the same gestalt approach. One could, of course, program the computer to solve the problem by brute-force -- amounting, in essence, to a curve-tracing procedure followed by numerical integration -- and having done so it would be possible to solve the problem rapidly and reliably and with a degree of accuracy which it is quite beyond the unaided human to duplicate. (The repeated emphasis on computers arises from the experience that one

cannot program a problem for a computer until he has stated his criteria and methodology completely, explicitly, and objectively.)

Sometimes it is more difficult to formulate the criterion for a problem than to state
the question itself. Consider the following problem, which is a good deal simpler and
more explicit than most. One has a sample of size n, drawn from a population known
to be normal, and one wishes to estimate both parameters. In the case of the mean, it
is clear that by any reasonable criterion the best estimator is $\Sigma \; x_i/n$. But in the
case of the variance there is no such unique and simple answer. $\Sigma \; (x_i - \bar{x})^2/(n-1)$,
the formula taught in the usual cookbook course on statistics, is "best" in the sense of
unbiasedness; $\Sigma \; (x_i - \bar{x})^2/n$ is "best" in the maximum-likelihood sense; and
$\Sigma \; (x_i - \bar{x})^2/(n+1)$ is "best" in the sense of minimum expected value of mean-square
deviation from the true parameter. How much more difficult, then, to choose an optimum information channel, or make an optimum decision in inventory handling or air
traffic control system design.

It is clear that many different approaches must be carried on simultaneously. This
book is a sampling of the approaches being taken by some of the most brilliant men
working in this field -- men who have already made notable advances and are exceedingly likely to make more. They vary from the heuristic approach of Flood to the
formally stated theorems of Wolfowitz; from the meticulous caution of Doob to the
provocative conjectures of Sobel; from some which are in my opinion exceedingly important, such as Shannon's, to others which may prove to be trivial. But they are all
exciting. For this field of endeavour is the most exciting which any scholar can pur-
sue -- the study of information and decision processes.

COMPUTATION IN DECISION MAKING

George W. Brown

The context with which this paper is concerned is one in which solutions to real-life decision problems are sought through application of mathematics. The use of the word "computation" in the title implies for us an interest in the process of obtaining usable results, to be applied to situations arising in the "real" world. In contrast, the computational process employed experimentally in support of research in Decision Theory itself will not be discussed here. As a consequence of its orientation this paper will necessarily consist mainly of philosophical reflections on the nature, state, and prospects of the difficult art of making mathematical applications to the making of decisions.

Recent years have witnessed an impressive growth of results, prestige, and future expectations associated with what has been termed the "quantitative", "objective", or "scientific" approach to problems of the real world. The boom is descended from the contacts between the mathematician's world and the real world, established during World War II on a scale hitherto unprecedented and since propagated in all directions. Accompanying the boom and its tremendous achievements is a whole new vocabulary of "O. K. " words (which need no specific citation here) and, unfortunately, some conceptions which, at the very least, constitute massive oversimplifications of the nature and circumstances of the art with which we are here concerned. Recent and probable future developments in electronic computational and data processing devices, and the spectacular achievements associated with their applications, whet the collective appetite still further. Thus we are led to the simple picture of a typical adventure in decision-making: the problem is first formulated appropriately through construction of a mathematical model, next analyzed to obtain a method of solution, and finally solved, using a sufficiently powerful computer (if required). In the most simple-minded view of the situation the very mention of the term "mathematical model" is almost of itself enough to vanquish all difficulties of formulation, and optimism is almost universally

1

warranted in expecting methods of solution to appear, together with machines fast enough to produce the solutions.

This paper will dip into some of the links similar to those by which the real world is connected for us to mathematics, with particular reference to decision making, in an attempt to gain insight into some pertinent limitations, prospects, and probable future investigations. There will be explorations of the probable failure, often, of the most obvious and straightforward techniques to provide solutions within inherent machine capabilities, discussion of conceptual inadequacies and other modeling difficulties, consideration of alternative approaches involving computers in "simulation" and "gaming" contexts, and some attention to the possible uses of computers in "imaginative" processes comprehending "heuristic programming", "artificial intelligence", or "learning" programs. The position to be supported is that present expectations associated with the boom described above rest excessively upon the past record of more easily obtained results (which naturally arise in the early skimming of a new field of problems); that, nevertheless, ultimate fulfillment and surpassing of present expectations will certainly occur; but that they will occur as a result of developments still to come and not primarily in accord with the simple-minded view stated earlier.

As a preliminary, let us consider briefly how computers may enter into the solution of a decision problem. It has been suggested, by a wag who shall remain anonymous, that computers solve decision problems by having the answers given to them. Properly interpreted, this suggestion is nearly correct. In some decision problems, there does exist a well-formulated model and a _practical_ algorithm for numerical computation, corresponding to the simple-minded view of decision making which was stated earlier. In very many problems, however, it may be the case that an algorithm is unknown, or known but impractical, or that insufficient information is available, or that the simple picture fails to be adequate for any one of a dozen other reasons. In these cases, if the computer is to yield a decision there must exist some reasonable rule of thumb, as adopted, for example, in certain classes of scheduling problems, or some set of approximations which lead to acceptable decision-making behavior. Computational approaches may be used to develop such approximations, or to aid the intuition of the ultimate decision-maker in a number of ways. New applications will certainly continue to join the first class mentioned, that is, the well-behaved class; but

2

it seems likely that most such new applications will require ever increasing efforts to place them there. For this reason it will be increasingly important to develop satisfactory techniques for dealing with problems in the second class.

To illustrate a situation in which an algorithm exists, but so far in unmanageable form, consider the game of chess, which should be relatively simple, compared to a great many situations in the real world. According to the theory of games, there must exist for each player a solution in pure strategies (requiring no random mixing), guaranteeing both Black and White the best outcome that can be guaranteed. This result follows from the fact that chess is a member of a class of games characterized as being games of complete information. There exists an algorithm, which in principle works for all games of this type, and which simply requires isolation of a pair of strategies (one for each player) with the following properties: that Black's chosen strategy does at least as well as any possible Black strategy against the chosen White strategy; and that White's chosen strategy does at least as well as any possible White strategy against the chosen Black strategy. With luck one might establish such a pair by computing the outcomes of a number of strategy pairs equal to one less than the total number of all possible White and all possible Black strategies. The only difficulty is that the number of strategies conceivably open to each player is astronomical, with the result that the solution is simply unattainable by straight enumeration techniques, following the bare prescription of game theory. Of course the possibility exists that practically all non-optimal strategies might be susceptible to being ruled out by some analytical procedure, thus reducing the problem to manageable proportions. So far, this has not happened, and if it should, it would in any case remove the example from the class of straightforward, simple-minded applications of theory corresponding to a large general class of problems.

To show further how the number of strategies may mount up in a simple game, let us analyze briefly a simple card game which, on the face of it, ought to be considerably simpler than chess. The game in question, called Gops or Goofspiel[1], has been selected because the strategies are somewhat easier to count than in chess. In Goofspiel each of two players starts with a complete suit of 13 cards; a third complete suit is shuffled and placed face down; the fourth suit is discarded. Play begins by facing up the top card of the table pack, after which each player chooses independently a card

3

from his own hand. Ranking the cards in ascending order from Ace to King, the player who has played higher captures the exposed table card, together with a number of points corresponding to its rank (1 through 13). Play continues in this manner, with a new card turned up each time on the table, and with the remaining cards in the players' hands diminishing by one each time, until all cards are exhausted after 13 plays. In case of a tie at any time the next card is also turned up, and all table cards ride until the tie is broken. The winner of the game, of course, is the player who has captured the most points.

Goofspiel is sufficiently interesting so that players might as well relieve themselves of the strain of remembering past plays, by the process of leaving exposed cards which have been played. Intuitively, the general idea is to "buy" the table cards at as low a "price" as possible, with a strong preference for beating the opponent on individual turns by very little, while being beaten by large margins oneself. (Hence the name of the game. If I play the queen and my opponent plays the jack, he has "goofed"; but if I play the queen and he plays either the king or the deuce, I have "goofed".)

It is easily shown that this game does not possess solutions in pure strategies. For if there exists a pure strategy for the first player, the second player can know that strategy, and can arrange to play king on queen, queen on jack, etc., winning twelve of the thirteen cards (and losing the thirteenth by playing ace on king). Nevertheless, the theory of games assures us that there are solutions in mixed strategies, and that a number of finite processes exist for determining a solution. Our purpose here is not to estimate the total difficulty of solving the game completely, but rather to discuss the colossal number of pure strategies open to each player and to demonstrate the impossibility even of listing them one by one, much less going on to complete the solution by direct methods.

Before attempting to count the strategies we might review briefly the definition of the term, as used in the theory of games. A strategy is a complete specification, providing a unique play for each situation which might conceivably arise during the entire game, and existing in advance of any actual play. Thus a single strategy must anticipate all combinations of one's own moves with all moves of the opponent and with every possible order of the table pack. Equivalently, a strategy is any set of rules which you could give to a small boy to enable him to play every game exactly as you would have

4

played the same game.

Taking the simplest method of enumerating possible strategies, we note that on the first play we need to allow for 13 different cards which might be exposed, and we might specify any one of 13 cards to be played. A little thought shows that a single strategy, specifying the first move, consists of a table with an arbitrary entry opposite each possible exposed card, as in the following example:

Exposed	To be played
A	A
2	A
3	7
4	5
5	5
6	2
7	Q
8	A
9	9
10	K
J	K
Q	K
K	K

Since each of 13 positions in the right-hand column may be filled in any one of 13 different ways, there are 13^{13} different tables of this sort, each one a possible candidate for specifying the first move. Thus, without getting beyond the first move we observe that there are 13^{13} possible ways of starting, each one of which corresponds to all the different strategies which agree on the first move. Suppose now that any particular one of these 13^{13} starting points had been selected, and consider the situation at the second move. The opponent might have played any one of 13 different cards on the first play, and any one of 12 cards may now have been turned up on the table; specification of a strategy requires that every one of these $13 \cdot 12 = 156$ possibilities be anticipated, following each of the 13 possibilities which was already anticipated by the specifications of the opening move. Unfortunately even at the second move we cannot ignore the initial 13 possibilities for the exposed table card on the first play, since our strategy must now tabulate the moves to be made for every conceivable situation which might arise. We obtain $13 \cdot 156 = 2028$ situations for which the second move must be prepared. The original specification of the first move permits description of the complete state of the game to date, for each of these 2028 situations, any one of which can occur. Noting now that for each of these our player has 12 cards from which to choose, we see that a specification for the second move, having chosen a specification for the

5

first move, entails preparation of a table with 2028 entries, each of which may take on any one of 12 values. This implies that there are 12^{2028} possible specifications of the second move, for each possible specification of the first move, leading to the ridiculous number $13^{13} \cdot 12^{2028}$ for the number of different ways of specifying the first two moves. Without proceeding further along this road it is clear that it might pay to inspect the problem to see if some obvious simplification exists.

For the sake of the curious we shall make such a simplification and investigate the consequences. Note that the original game is solvable by providing solutions independently to each of 13 different games, corresponding to the first card exposed in the table deck, which, after all, is known to both players before either makes any actual play. Since a strategy for the overall game would correspond to any combination of strategies, one for each of the 13 particular games, and since each of the latter has the same total number of possible strategies, it may be seen that the number of strategies of the overall game will be the 13th power of the number of strategies of any one of the particular games. Offhand it appears easier to solve 13 such games separately than to solve the original game at once.

Thus we may start again to enumerate strategies, assuming that the first card of the table pack is fixed and known. For the first move we find only 13 possibilities for our player and for the second move we have only the $13 \cdot 12 = 156$ different situations corresponding to 13 choices of the other player on the first move, and 12 possibilities for the second table card to be exposed. Again our player can choose one out of 12 cards for each of the 156 situations, with the result that there are now only $13 \cdot 12^{156}$ ways of specifying the first two moves. Unfortunately each of the 156 situations becomes, on the third move, $12 \cdot 11 = 132$ new situations, corresponding to the 12 selections the other player might have made on the second move and to the 11 new possibilities for the third card to be exposed in the table pack. Since now our player must choose from 11 different possibilities in his own hand it appears that the third move brings in the juicy factor $11^{132 \cdot 156}$, and again it's time to stop. We already have $13 \cdot 12^{156} \cdot 11^{156 \cdot 132}$ different ways to specify how to get through three moves of the game, even confining our attention to a particular top card in the table pack. It will be near enough for our purposes if we substitute $10^{20,000}$ for the number just obtained, and observe that the number of possible strategies for the entire game must be a great deal larger yet.

For the sake of perspective assume that strategies could be disposed of at one per microsecond, then note that there are about 3×10^{13} microseconds in a year, or about 10^{16} microseconds in 300 years. There is obviously no hope of denting $10^{20,000}$ in units of 10^{16} at a time. Expected progress in computer design along the lines already established might yield, say, as much as two orders of magnitude improvement in speed every five years, so that by a wild extrapolation we might look for 40 orders of magnitude improvement in 100 years, and in 300 years 120 orders of magnitude. Obviously, the figure $10^{20,000}$ is just as far away as ever. It is almost unbelievable that such an innocent-appearing little game could generate this kind of combinatorial madness. And surely this is a simple game compared to many real-life decision problems.

It might be asked at this point how it is that people can dare to play games of this sort. One possible answer is that so many, indeed practically all, of the strategies impartially listed above are obviously terrible and as a result, never get considered. Of course the optimum strategies probably escape consideration as well. When the game is played by real players it is impossible even to say which strategies are being used, much less estimate how good their strategies would be against a theoretical solution of the game.

Turning from this exercise in futility we shall now touch lightly upon some of the difficulties which may be met in modeling a problem for analysis. Consider, for example, the difficulty of determining an objective function for a large, publicly owned firm. While the notion of decision-making to maximize profits seems acceptable, it may be difficult to make the notion sufficiently precise, except under steady-state assumptions. Under typical circumstances there are choices which permit trading profits in one period for profits in another, characterized by a number of degrees of freedom. Moreover there are options concerning the portion of profits to be distributed and the portion to be retained for capital growth. Taken together with the diverse aspirations of the stockholders for long-term gains or for income at various times, these circumstances suggest that management does not have a mathematically precise criterion for insertion in a model. The notion that management attempts to maximize profits may serve to rule out a large number of clearly bad decisions but may be, in that simple form, inadequate for comparison of courses of action which are all pretty

7

good.

Lack of information may hamper the modeling process in several other ways. In a business firm there may be inadequate information on the firm's costs, still less about the competitors' costs, or it may be impossible to predict the outcomes of all possible decisions; in some cases it is doubtful whether all of the alternatives open to a firm or to its competitors can be known in advance. The methods of the theory of games presume that the alternatives are known to all players, and that the expected outcomes to all players associated with the interacting choices are also known to all. Certainly many real problems are very badly off in this respect.

Perhaps more fundamental difficulties may be found at the conceptual level. The theory of games provides perfectly acceptable models for the case of two players in a zero-sum game, in which the gain of either player is exactly the loss of the other. Unfortunately, far too few competitive situations fall into this category. On the other hand, with non-zero-sum games the theoretical situation is far from satisfactory; we may find either no appealing solutions, or too many different solutions, with no good way to distinguish a preferred solution.

An interesting artificial example which is somewhat paradoxical is provided by the Prisoners' Dilemma[2]. In this example the players are two criminals who have been arrested for a crime jointly committed. The prisoners are assumed to be held separately, with no possibility of communication between them, and each is approached by the prosecuting attorney with the same proposition. As part of his pitch the prosecutor persuades each prisoner that without further cooperation on the part of either there is sufficient evidence of commission of a crime to ensure a sentence of one year apiece. As an inducement to confess he estimates that if one prisoner confesses while the other does not the one who does confess will get off with three months, but the other prisoner will get 10 years. Finally, if both prisoners should confess he estimates 8 years apiece. The table below summarizes the situation:

Prisoner B

		does not confess	confesses
	does not confess	1 year for A 1 year for B	10 years for A 3 months for B
Prisoner A			
	confesses	3 months for A 10 years for B	8 years for A 8 years for B

8

Both prisoners are in possession of the same table. Assuming now that the table contains all pertinent outcomes, so that we reject possibilities of later reprisal (and any suggestions that the situation is unrealistic), it is possible in this case to isolate a "rational" course of action for each prisoner. If each prisoner is optimizing for himself, he must confess, since whichever decision he imputes to his partner he will always do better by confessing. Suppose A imputes to B a decision not to confess, then A's decision to confess will get him 3 months instead of 1 year. If B is assumed to confess, then A's decision to confess gets him 8 years instead of 10 years. Thus, on either assumption about B it turns out that A does better to confess. The consequence that two rational prisoners wind up with 8 years apiece instead of the 1 year apiece they might have had is somewhat troublesome. Within the framework of the problem, however, there seems to be no other conclusion.

The Prisoners' Dilemma illustrates the danger in assuming that optimization by each individual within an inter-acting decision structure necessarily leads to optimum results for any individual. A similar example for n players is based on a hypothetical group of farmers, each farmer independently deciding whether or not to restrict production. If no one farmer can significantly affect the price level, then each will choose full production; the aggregate effect of these choices may so depress the price level that all would have been better off to restrict production.

The few examples presented so far have significance only insofar as we recognize that very many abstractions of real problems are more complex, and further, that real-life problems continue to originate with constantly increasing complexity. Under such conditions it is absurd to depend on routine applications of established methods to meet the bulk of future decision problems. On the other hand, the negative impression generated thus far should be offset by an optimistic appraisal of the possibilities of success of non-routine approaches of one kind or another.

The most dramatic kind of non-routine solution is describable only as being ingenious in origin. Normally a solution of this sort results from exploitation of a special characteristic of the particular problem not found in the large class of general problems to which the particular problem belongs. How such solutions are invented may not often be understood, but the net effect is often comparable to the result of a sudden inspiration. Whatever their origin, such ingenious methods turn up often enough to be

9

interesting, and provide practical methods for situations in which the obvious more general method would be hopeless.

For those who may recall some calculus, the evaluation of $\int_0^\infty e^{-x^2}\,dx$ provides an interesting example. In this case, the direct methods of evaluation, suitable to a large class of definite integrals, are cumbersome and tedious. Suppose the unknown integral is called I. Then $I = \int_0^\infty e^{-x^2}\,dx = \int_0^\infty e^{-y^2}\,dy$, where the second integral simply replaces the dummy variable "x" by "y". But now

$$I^2 = \int_0^\infty \int_0^\infty e^{-(x^2 + y^2)}\,dx\,dy$$

and a transformation to polar coordinates yields

$$I^2 = \int_0^{\pi/2} \int_0^\infty r e^{-r^2}\,dr\,d\theta\ .$$

Of course, $r e^{-r^2}$ has an indefinite integral $-\frac{1}{2} e^{-r^2}$ (where e^{-x^2} has no indefinite integral), and the result $I^2 = \frac{\pi}{4}$ is obtained, from which $I = \frac{1}{2}\sqrt{\pi}$, a surprising result. It is far from clear how the trick was originally motivated; countless students have been impressed by it. Similarly mysterious ingenious methods have been used for generations in the solution of certain special types of differential equations.

The familiar game of Nim (and some of its close relatives) in which players alternate taking matches from one of possibly many piles until the last player removes the last match, provides another example. The object of the game may be to take the last match, or it may be to force the opponent to do so. In either case, there exists a simple method by which one of the players (corresponding to the initial conditions of the game) can force a win. Based on this method simple Nim-playing machines which have been constructed exhibit faultless play. The solution rests upon representation of the number of matches in each pile as a binary number, on the basis of which it is possible to characterize the set of states which a player should seek to establish. Once approached in this way the problem is quite simple; in contrast, an attack from the point of view of game theory alone would encounter a monstrous number of combinatorial variations.

A particularly amusing example is furnished by the following game, played with an ordinary rectangular table and a large supply of pennies. Starting with an empty table two players alternate placing one penny each time, anywhere on the table. Pennies may touch one another, but may not overlap, nor may any penny be moved, once placed. A penny may overlap the edge, providing it remains on the table. The object of the game is to be the last to be able to put a penny down. This game, which appears difficult to analyze, actually has a beautiful solution, at least in principle. If a player has first turn and plays in the exact center, he may then mimic any play of his opponent, choosing each time the symmetric position on the opposite side of the center. This player thus is able after each turn to present his opponent with a symmetric position, with the property that any position open to his opponent will have a counterpart opposite it, ensuring that the mimicking player can play as long as his opponent can. Here again we observe that the solution has a special flavor, deriving from the radial symmetry of the table. This solution would obviously not pertain to a table of free form.

The examples discussed above provide encouragement of two sorts. In the first place, they indicate the value of human analysis and the possibility of human transformation of a problem to tractability from a state of apparent impregnability. We can continue to expect solutions of the ingenious variety, provided we do not neglect to seek them. In the second place, some solutions of the "ingenious" type may actually be found by computational approaches. Note, in particular, the role that symmetry played in the last example. It is not inconceivable that problem-solving methods currently under development [3] would permit "invention" of important solutions of this sort by high-speed machines. It is appropriate to point out here that people constantly solve, in some sense, problems that are insoluble by mathematical standards. Limitations of time, deficiencies in information, overwhelming combinatorial complexity, all these are commonplace in everyday life. Human decision-making is characterized imprecisely by the terms "experience," "intuition," and "imagination". In ways not well understood the functioning human compromises on a wholesale scale, reducing to manageable size the number of alternatives he will entertain, perhaps choosing a decision first and then rationalizing it, perhaps seeking a new decision if the rationalization fails to come off. We might profitably ask for ways in which computers can aid people in improving their decision-making, rather than insist on replacement of the human process by a machine process. For example, the most cogent question from this point of view is how can a chess player use a machine to better his play, as opposed to how can a machine substitute for him. One could hope that clever coupling of machine facilities to a skilled chess player might admit of interesting results not

11

achievable by chess-playing machine programs operating on their own.

Under the general heading of "simulation and gaming" there have been a number of experimental studies in a wide range of areas, including military situations, machine-shop scheduling problems, warehousing operations, traffic flows, and refinery operations, to name only a few. Simulation techniques provide experimental tools which may give new insights into problems already well formulated, may aid in the development of a model in not-so-well-formulated problems, may provide leads to the construction of reasonable criteria or satisfactory rules of thumb, or may permit consideration for human decision of a larger number of alternatives than would otherwise be possible. Simulation processes essentially provide an experimental laboratory which can bring some problems out to where human intellects can operate on them. The role of the computer in simulation is primarily that of referee and score keeper in posing situations and translating decisions to consequences. The wide diversity of simulation studies already in existence is sufficient to indicate the high and growing incidence of problems in which simulation is useful.

Another hope for the future improvement of decision-making rests upon the further development of techniques for translating implicit assumptions, values, or prejudices of individuals (or groups of individuals) into explicit form for analysis of their consequences. As has been pointed out above there are often conceptual and other difficulties which block the completion of appropriate decision-making models. In some cases it has been possible to capitalize on the fact that people do indeed make decisions even when they shouldn't apparently be able to do so. An assumed underlying consistent structure may be brought out by getting answers for a set of simple hypothetical situations. Once made explicit the underlying structure may be used to provide input parameters in more complex situations. An example of this proposes solution of a difficult allocation problem [4] by using value estimates derived from responses of a "policy board" to specially designed miniature allocation problems. The argument is that whatever rationale the policy board might have used, it can be reflected in a corresponding rationale applied to the more complex problem. The approach is conceptually similar to the process that may be used to estimate a priori probabilities and utilities in statistical decision problems [5] of incomplete information. It is hoped that developments of this kind will increasingly contribute to the solution of difficult problems,

12

sometimes involving otherwise indefinable notions, such as the value of a human life, for example.

The most challenging area of research is at the same time the one with the greatest potential for future effect on decision-making. This is the area of "artificial intelligence", under which we group heuristic problem-solving methods, already alluded to, learning programs, pattern-recognition programs, and self-organizing logical processes. These developments, at present in early infancy, proceed in one way or another by analogy with what is understood of certain psychological processes, setting up inductive processes of diagnosis and formal manipulation of problem statements, or depending on random alteration and reinforcement, or borrowing variously from notions of perception, abstraction, or the like. In this way it is hoped to develop for certain tasks or classes of tasks machine methods or organizations which would not normally be found as a result of ad hoc efforts on the particular tasks.

For concreteness' sake a few examples will be cited. Heuristic programming has been applied to the task of proving theorems in Boolean algebra and to the solution of problems in Euclidean geometry, among others, and has been proposed for numerous situations, including chess [6]. Random trial and reinforcement models of learning have been applied to simple tests [7], and the Perceptron, a statistical separation model corresponding to self-organizing neural nets [8] has been successful in learning to discriminate between visual patterns. Activities of this kind, generally recent in origin, are mushrooming at the present time; it can be expected that in a few years the overall effort expended in these directions will be impressively large. Obvious applications for the future are automatic language translation, automatic preparation of abstracts of scientific articles, devices for reading printed characters, information-retrieval systems, etc. The actual potential domain of applicability is far greater than is indicated by these examples. If researchers can successfully model a few powerful principles of evolutionary program development, corresponding to the interaction of environment, genetic structures, and natural selection, we may expect truly marvelous consequences.

BIBLIOGRAPHY

[1] Luce, R. Duncan, and Howard Raiffa, Games and Decisions, John Wiley & Sons, 1957, p. 44.

[2] Ibid, p. 95.

[3] Gelernter, H.L. and N. Rochester, "Intelligent Behavior in Problem-Solving Machines", I.B.M. Journal of Research and Development, October 1958.

[4] Smith, Jack W., "A Plan to Allocate and Procure Electronic Sets by the Use of Linear Programming Techniques and Analytical Methods of Assigning Values to Qualitative Factors", Naval Research Logistics Quarterly, Sept. 1956.

[5] Savage, Leonard J., "The Foundations of Statistics", Wiley, 1954.

[6] Newell, Allen, J.C. Shaw, and H.A. Simon, "Chess-Playing Programs and the Problem of Complexity", I.B.M. Journal of Research and Development, Oct. 1958.

[7] Friedberg, R.M., "A Learning Machine: Part I", I.B.M. Journal of Research and Development, Jan. 1958. Friedberg, R.M., B. Dunham, and J.H. North, "A Learning Machine: Part II", ibid, July, 1959.

[8] "The Perceptron, a Theory of Statistical Separability in Cognitive Systems", Cornell Aeronautical Laboratory Report No. VG - 1196 - G - 1, Jan. 1958.

MOTIVATION FOR AN APPROACH

TO THE SEQUENTIAL DESIGN OF EXPERIMENTS

Herman Chernoff

1. Introduction.

Considerable scientific research may be characterized in the following way. A scientist is interested in a problem. He performs an experiment to obtain information. This information not only serves to illuminate the problem but is used to design a more informative experiment. As information is accumulated, he continues designing more and more effective experiments until he reaches the point where he feels that further experimentation seems no longer necessary. Then he announces his results. The procedure outlined may reasonably be entitled sequential design of experiments. In spite of its apparent usefulness, there seems to be no formal theory of sequential design of experiments in the literature of statistics.

In this paper I wish to report on the motivation for an approach to a formal theory of sequential design of experiments which is presented in [2] .

For the sake of mathematical simplicity it is often effective to develop first a large sample theory and this is what I propose to discuss. It might seem peculiar to talk of a large sample theory in connection with sequential analysis which was originally developed in order to make it possible to stop sampling after few observations if those observations happened to be very informative. However the sample size in the standard theory of sequential analysis tends to be large if the cost of experimentation is small compared to the costs of making the wrong decisions. Thus we shall use the terms asymptotic theory and large sample theory synonymously to denote the theory applying to the case where the cost of experimentation approaches zero.

The classical theory of statistics usually deals with two kinds of inference. These are testing hypotheses and estimation. For reasons we shall not discuss here, it seems that for estimation problems a large sample sequential design theory will not be substantially different from a large but fixed sample size theory. Thus we shall confine

15

our future discussion to the problem of testing hypotheses.

Let us consider the following problem which may serve as a prototype of the problem of the sequential design of experiments applied to testing hypotheses. It is desired to determine which of two methods of manufacturing traveling wave tubes is more reliable. Suppose that p_1 is the probability that a traveling wave tube made by method 1 will meet the desired specifications and p_2 is the probability that such a tube made by method 2 is satisfactory. Then the unknown state of nature is represented by $\theta = (p_1, p_2)$. It is desired to adopt method 1 if the hypothesis $H_1 : p_1 \geq p_2$ is true and to adopt method 2 if the alternative hypothesis $H_2 : p_1 < p_2$ is true. Two experiments are available. These are E_1, test a tube made by method 1, and E_2, test a tube made by method 2. After each experiment, the statistician must decide whether to continue experimentation or to stop. If he continues, he must decide which experiment to perform. If he stops he must select one of the two methods for adoption.

2. Sequential analysis for large samples.

We shall find it illuminating to study a well developed theory of sequential analysis for the case of large samples. This is the theory of sequentially testing a simple hypothesis versus a simple alternative where there is no choice of experiments. For this problem, Wald developed the sequential likelihood-ratio test and later collaborated with Wolfowitz to prove its optimality (see [5] and [6]).

To be more specific let us suppose that an experiment is repeated many times, yielding independent observations $X_1, X_2, \ldots, X_n, \ldots$. Let H_1 specify that the observations have density $f_1(x)$. Let H_2, the alternative hypothesis, specify density $f_2(x)$. A test is said to be a sequential likelihood-ratio test if there are two numbers A and B such that after the nth observation the test dictates

$$\text{accept } H_1 \text{ if } \quad \sum_{i=1}^{n} \log \frac{f_1(X_i)}{f_2(X_i)} \geq A,$$

$$\text{accept } H_2 \text{ if } \quad \sum_{i=1}^{n} \log \frac{f_1(X_i)}{f_2(X_i)} \leq B, \text{ and}$$

$$\text{continue experimentation if } B < \sum_{i=1}^{n} \log \frac{f_1(X_i)}{f_2(X_i)} < A.$$

Note that experimentation is stopped if H_1 or H_2 is accepted. Also the name likelihood-ratio test derives from the fact that

16

$\prod_{i=1}^{n} f_1(X_i)$ is called the likelihood of H_1 given the data $X_1, X_2, \ldots, X_n$. Hence

$\sum_{i=1}^{n} \log [f_1(X_i)/f_2(X_i)]$ is the logarithm of the ratio of the likelihood of H_1 to the

likelihood of H_2 and is called the logarithm of the likelihood ratio. Now let us assume

that c is the cost per experiment. Let r_1 and r_2 be the costs attached to the two errors,

reject H_1 (i.e., accept H_2) when H_1 is true, and accept H_1 when H_2 is true respectively.

Then it is shown in [1] , [3] , and [6] that all admissible procedures are sequential

likelihood-ratio tests. However this fact does not pick out a best choice of A and B. To

do so let us assume a priori probabilities w_1 and w_2 for the hypotheses H_1 and H_2 re-

spectively ($w_1 + w_2 = 1$) and let c $\rightarrow$ 0.

For an arbitrary procedure, the risk or expected cost under H_1 is given by

(1a) $R_1 = r_1 \alpha + cN_1$

where α is the probability of rejecting H_1 when it is true and N_1 is the expected sample

size when H_1 is true. Similarly the risk under H_2 is

(1b) $R_2 = r_2 \beta + cN_2$

where β is the probability of accepting H_1 when it is false and N_2 is the expected sample

size under H_2.

If c is small, the optimum sequential likelihood-ratio test should tend to have large

sample sizes. This is achieved by making A very large and B highly negative. As

c $\rightarrow$ 0, we expect A and -B to approach infinity.

Let us continue heuristically. We shall suppose that A and -B approach infinity at

comparable rates. Then applying Wald's approximations of [5] , we have

(2) $\alpha \approx e^B$ $\beta \approx e^{-A}$

(3) $N_1 \approx A/I_1$ $N_2 \approx -B/I_2$

where

(4) $I_1 = \int \log [f_1(x)/f_2(x)] \, f_1(x)dx$

and

(5) $I_2 = \int \log [f_2(x)/f_1(x)] \, f_2(x)dx$

are the Kullback-Leibler information numbers (see [4]). Then

(6) $R_1 \approx r_1 e^B + cA/I_1$

and

17

$$(7) \qquad R_2 \approx r_2 e^{-A} - cB/I_2.$$

Applying the a priori probabilities, the average risk is given by

$$(8) \qquad \mathcal{R} = w_1 R_1 + w_2 R_2.$$

We shall approximate the optimal procedure, that is the optimal choice of A and B, by minimizing the approximations of $\mathcal{R}$ obtained by substituting the approximations of equations (6) and (7). Setting the partial derivatives with respect to A and B equal to zero, we obtain

$$(9) \qquad A = \log [I_1 w_2 r_2 / w_1 c] \approx -\log c$$

and

$$(10) \qquad B = \log [w_2 c / I_2 w_1 r_1] \approx \log c.$$

For this procedure we have

$$(11) \qquad \alpha \sim c, \qquad \beta \sim c$$

$$(12) \qquad N_1 \approx \frac{-\log c}{I_1}, \qquad N_2 \approx \frac{-\log c}{I_2}$$

and

$$(13) \qquad R_1 \approx \frac{-c \log c}{I_1}, \qquad R_2 \approx \frac{-c \log c}{I_2}.$$

Before proceeding to apply these asymptotic results, several remarks deserve mention.

1. The sequential likelihood-ratio test can be interpreted from an a posteriori probability point of view. Applying Bayes theorem, if H_1 and H_2 have a priori probabilities w_1 and w_2 and the data $X_1, X_2, \ldots, X_n$ which yield the likelihoods L_{1n} and L_{2n} are observed, then H_1 and H_2 have a posteriori probabilities w_{1n} and w_{2n} given by

$$(14) \qquad w_{1n} = \frac{w_1 L_{1n}}{w_1 L_{1n} + w_2 L_{2n}}$$

and

$$(15) \qquad w_{2n} = \frac{w_2 L_{2n}}{w_1 L_{1n} + w_2 L_{2n}}$$

and then

$$(16) \qquad \frac{w_{1n}}{w_{2n}} = \frac{w_1}{w_2} \lambda_n$$

where

$$(17) \qquad \lambda_n = \frac{L_{1n}}{L_{2n}}$$

is the likelihood ratio. Then a stopping rule which calls for stopping when

18

log $\lambda_n \approx \pm$ log c is equivalent to one which calls for stopping when one of the a posteriori probabilities is roughly of the order of magnitude of c.

2. The information number I_1 is the expectation under H_1 of log $[f_1(X)/f_2(X)]$ which is the logarithm of the likelihood ratio corresponding to one observation. Thus I_1 measures the rate at which $\sum_{i=1}^{n}$ log $[f_1(X_i)/f_2(X_i)]$ tends to increase under H_1. This explains why I_1 appears in the approximation of equation (3). Similarly I_2, the expectation under H_2 of log $[f_2(X)/f_1(X)] = -$ log $[f_1(X)/f_2(X)]$, measures the rate at which $\sum_{i=1}^{n}$ log $[f_1(X_i)/f_2(X_i)]$ tends to go toward $-B$ when H_2 is the true hypothesis. Since the risks R_1 and R_2 for the optimal procedure are approximately inversely proportional to I_1 and I_2 respectively, high values of I_1 and I_2 are desirable. Incidentally, I_1 and I_2 are known to be non-negative (see [4]).

3. Since the probability of accepting the wrong hypothesis is roughly of the order of magnitude c and the expected sample size is of the order of magnitude of $-$log c for the optimal procedure, it follows that the main contribution to the risk is made up of the cost of sampling.

4. It is important to note that the optimal procedure and its risks i.e., A, B, R_1, and R_2 are relatively insensitive to changes in the particular values of the arbitrarily chosen a priori probabilities w_1 and w_2 and to the values of r_1 and r_2. This is indicated by equations (9), (10), and (13).

5. The above argument which consists of approximating the A and B for which $\mathcal{R}$ is minimal by the values of A and B which minimize the approximation to $\mathcal{R}$ is not rigorous. However a rigorous and detailed proof of the above results can be derived using Wald's bounds in [5] .

3. The design problem for deciding between two simple hypotheses.

Having discussed the simplest sequential testing problem from the large-sample point of view, let us proceed to introduce a design element into it. First suppose that there are available two equally costly experiments E_1 and E_2. Suppose that the experimenter wishes to test a simple hypothesis H_1 versus a simple alternative H_2 but that he must restrict himself to the use of one of these experiments exclusively. If he selects E_1 and proceeds thereafter in an optimal fashion, his risks under H_1 and H_2 will be inversely proportional to $I_1(E_1)$ and $I_1(E_2)$. Hence if $I_1(E_1) > I_1(E_2)$ and $I_2(E_1)$ $> I_2(E_2)$ it would obviously pay for him to select the experiment E_1.

Suppose however that $I_1(E_1) > I_1(E_2)$ but $I_2(E_1) < I_2(E_2)$. In this case E_1 is better if H_1 is true and E_2 is better if H_2 is true. If we knew that H_1 were the true hypothesis, we could use E_1. At first glance the last sentence sounds foolish. If we knew that H_1 were the true hypothesis, we would not bother experimenting at all. At this point the large sample or small cost aspect of the problem becomes important again. If c is very small, it may pay to continue experimentation even though the experimenter were almost certain that H_1 is true. Thus if we extend our problem to the one where we may select an experiment after each observation, it would make sense to select E_1 if the previous data favored H_1 strongly and to select E_2 if the previous data favored H_2 strongly. More generally, if several experiments were available, and the data favored H_i strongly, it would seem reasonable to select the next experiment E so as to maximize $I_i(E)$.

For the case where c is very small, and very large samples will be called for, it isn't terribly important what is done for the first few observations. Thus we may now propose a procedure for sequentially testing a simple hypothesis versus a simple alternative where several experiments are available. This procedure is suggested by the results of section 2 and the above discussion.

Let $f_1(x, E)$ be the probability density of the data under H_1 if experiment E is used. Similarly let $f_2(x, E)$ be the density of the data under H_2. Let $E^{(i)}$ be the experiment used for the ith observation and let X_i be the ith observation. Then

$$(18) \qquad L_{1n} = \prod_{i=1}^{n} f_1(X_i, E^{(i)})$$

and

$$(19) \qquad L_{2n} = \prod_{i=1}^{n} f_2(X_i, E^{(i)})$$

are the likelihoods of H_1 and H_2 based on the first n observations. The procedure suggested calls for the following after the nth observation. Stop experimenting and accept H_1 if

$$(20) \qquad \log \lambda_n = \log \frac{L_{1n}}{L_{2n}} = \sum_{i=1}^{n} \frac{f_1(X_i, E^{(i)})}{f_2(X_i, E^{(i)})} \geq -\log c.$$

Stop experimenting and reject H_1 if

(21) $$\log \lambda_n = \log \frac{L_{1n}}{L_{2n}} = \sum_{i=1}^{n} \log \frac{f_1(X_i, E^{(i)})}{f_2(X_i, E^{(i)})} \leq \log c.$$

Otherwise continue experimenting and select $E^{(n+1)}$ as follows. If $L_{1n} > L_{2n}$, act as though H_1 were true to the extent of choosing $E^{(n+1)}$ to be that experiment E which maximizes $I_1(E)$. If $L_{2n} > L_{1n}$, select $E^{(n+1)}$ to maximize $I_2(E)$.

In this procedure we have made use of section 2 to suggest stopping when the likelihood ratio is roughly of the order of magnitude of c. We have applied the discussion of section 3 to suggest acting as though the more likely hypothesis were true in selecting the next experiment.

4. Composite hypotheses.

In the preceding section a procedure was suggested for the case of testing a simple hypothesis versus a simple alternative. The prototype example mentioned in section 1 is more complicated. Here the hypotheses are composite. That is to say the hypothesis and the experiment do not uniquely determine the distribution of the data. Thus, in the prototype example H_1 can be true with $p_1 = .6$ and $p_2 = .4$ or with $p_1 = .45$ and $p_2 = .43$. These two cases will lead to different distributions for the data. What is suggested by our previous discussions for this case? The use of the likelihood ratio for the stopping rule is easily generalized. However the problem of the choice of experiment seems to call for some additional concept.

To study this problem, let us think of the simplest case involving composite hypotheses. Suppose that the distribution of the data is determined by the experiment and a parameter θ. In general we denote H_1 and H_2 by

(22) $$H_1 : \theta \in \omega_1 \quad \text{and} \quad H_2 : \theta \in \omega_2 \qquad \text{[1]}$$

where ω_1 and ω_2 are two sets with no points in common. The simplest case involving a composite hypothesis is that where ω_1 consists of one point θ_1 and ω_2 consists of the two points θ_2 and θ_3. Then we are testing the simple hypothesis $\theta = \theta_1$ versus the composite alternative $\theta = \theta_2$ or θ_3. In our discussion of this case let us use the a priori and a posteriori probability point of view. The a priori probabilities of θ_1, θ_2, and θ_3 will be denoted here by w_1, w_2, and w_3. The a posteriori probabilities after n observations will be denoted by w_{1n}, w_{2n}, and w_{3n}. The first remark near the end of section 2 relates the a posteriori probabilities to the stopping rule. It seems natural to stop

---

[1] The symbol $\in$ denotes "is an element of."

when either w_{1n}, or $w_{2n} + w_{3n}$ is of the order of magnitude of c.

Suppose now that H_1 were the true hypothesis. Then it would be desired to have $w_{2n} + w_{3n}$ become small rapidly. Let us study how fast w_{2n} and w_{3n} approach zero when an experiment E, which yields data with density $f(x, \theta, E)$, is applied. As in section 2, we have

$$\frac{w_{2n}}{w_{1n}} = \frac{w_2}{w_1} \cdot \frac{\prod\limits_{i=1}^{n} f(X_i, \theta_2, E)}{\prod\limits_{i=1}^{n} f(X_i, \theta_1, E)}$$

(23) $$\frac{w_{2n}}{w_{1n}} = \frac{w_2}{w_1} e^{-S_{2n}}$$

where

(24) $$S_{2n} = \sum_{i=1}^{n} \log \frac{f(X_i, \theta_1, E)}{f(X_i, \theta_2, E)} .$$

When $\theta = \theta_1$, each term of the sum S_{2n} has expectation given by

(25) $$I(\theta_1, \theta_2, E) = \int \log \left[\frac{f(x, \theta_1, E)}{f(x, \theta_2, E)} \right] f(x, \theta_1, E) \, dx.$$

Similarly

(26) $$\frac{w_{3n}}{w_{1n}} = \frac{w_3}{w_1} e^{-S_{3n}}$$

where

(27) $$S_{3n} = \sum_{i=1}^{n} \log \frac{f(X_i, \theta_1, E)}{f(X_i, \theta_3, E)}$$

each term of which has expectation given by

(28) $$I(\theta_1, \theta_3, E) = \int \log \left[\frac{f(x, \theta_1, E)}{f(x, \theta_3, E)} \right] f(x, \theta_1, E) \, dx.$$

As $n \to \infty$, S_{2n} and S_{3n} approach infinity at rates determined by $I(\theta_1, \theta_2, E)$ and $I(\theta_1, \theta_3, E)$. Then w_{1n} approaches 1 and w_{2n} and w_{3n} approach zero at exponential rates determined by $I(\theta_1, \theta_2, E)$ and $I(\theta_1, \theta_3, E)$.

Suppose that $I(\theta_1, \theta_2, E) > I(\theta_1, \theta_3, E)$. Then w_{2n} approaches zero much faster than w_{3n}. In fact the rate at which $w_{2n} + w_{3n}$ approaches zero is then determined by $I(\theta_1, \theta_3, E)$, i.e., the smaller of $I(\theta_1, \theta_2, E)$ and $I(\theta_1, \theta_3, E)$. Thus the experiment which would be most effective would be the one which maximizes

$$\min \left\{ I(\theta_1, \theta_2, E), \; I(\theta_1, \theta_3, E) \right\}$$

This suggests a general procedure for selecting the experiment. First let

(29)
$$I(\theta, \phi, E) = \int \log \left[\frac{f(x, \theta, E)}{f(x, \phi, E)} \right] f(x, \theta, E) \, dx$$

Also we define the space alternative to θ by

$$a(\theta) = \omega_2 \text{ if } \theta \in \omega_1 \qquad \text{and}$$

(30)
$$a(\theta) = \omega_1 \text{ if } \theta \in \omega_2.$$

In our problem, the space alternative to θ_1 was $\omega_2 = \left\{ \theta_2, \theta_3 \right\}$ which corresponds to the hypothesis alternative to $\theta = \theta_1$. Similarly the space alternative to θ_2 is $\omega_1 = \left\{ \theta_1 \right\}$.

After n observations compute the maximum-likelihood estimate $\hat{\theta}_n$ of θ. Act as though $\hat{\theta}_n$ were the true value of θ by selecting the next experiment $E^{(n+1)}$ to make as large as possible the smallest of the

$$I(\hat{\theta}_n, \phi, E)$$

for all ϕ in $a(\hat{\theta}_n)$. In other words select $E^{(n+1)}$ to maximize

$$\min_{\phi \, \in \, a(\hat{\theta}_n)} I(\hat{\theta}_n, \phi, E).$$

The procedure of maximizing a minimum is reminiscent of the solution of a two-person zero-sum game. It corresponds to the behavior of a player selecting E to maximize a "payoff" $I(\hat{\theta}_n, \phi, E)$ when he has an opponent who will react to his choice with the worst possible alternative ϕ.

The theory of games tells us that frequently a player can improve his position by using randomized strategies. What does a randomized strategy represent for an experimenter? If one were to use a table of random numbers to select an experiment, this choice could be considered a randomized experiment. An example of a randomized experiment is E which consists of performing E_1 with probability .4, E_2 with probability .5, and E_3 with probability .1.[1] It is a fact that the randomized experiment E which selects $E_1, E_2, \ldots$ with probability $p_1, p_2, \ldots$ will yield

(31)
$$I(\theta, \phi, E) = \sum_i p_i I(\theta, \phi, E_i).$$

Then, as in game theory, broadening the class of available experiments to include the

---

[1] To select the experiment with a table of random numbers, one may take E_1, if a random digit chosen from the table is 0, 1, 2, or 3; take E_2 if the digit is 4, 5, 6, 7, or 8; and take E_3 if the digit is 9.

randomized experiments occasionally has the effect of enabling the experimenter to do somewhat better in maximizing

$$\min_{\phi \, \in \, a(\hat{\theta}_n)} I(\hat{\theta}_n, \phi, E).$$

5. The general procedure and its properties.

In section 2 we indicated that the stopping rule should lead to stopping experimentation when the logarithm of the likelihood ratio is of the order of magnitude of $-\log c$ or equivalently when the a posteriori probability is roughly of the order of magnitude of c. In section 3, we indicated that the experimenter should act as though his estimate of the parameter were the true value in selecting the next experiment to maximize the information. In section 4, we extended this notion to indicate how to maximize the information for testing composite hypotheses. Here the experimenter acts as though he were playing a game against an opponent selecting an alternative ϕ.

Let us summarize these ideas and present a general procedure whose properties we shall discuss. Let $\hat{\theta}_n$ be the maximum-likelihood estimate of θ. Let $\hat{\hat{\theta}}_n$ be the maximum-likelihood estimate of θ when θ is restricted to $a(\hat{\theta}_n)$, the space alternative to $\hat{\theta}_n$. Then

$$(32) \qquad S_n = \log \lambda_n = \sum_{i=1}^{n} \log [\, f(X_i, \hat{\theta}_n, E^{(i)})/f(X_i, \hat{\hat{\theta}}_n, E^{(i)})]$$

is the logarithm of the generalized likelihood ratio. Our procedure tells us to stop and accept the hypothesis corresponding to $\hat{\theta}_n$ if $S_n \geq -\log c$. Otherwise we must select an $(n+1)^{st}$ experiment $E^{(n+1)}$. This is to be that randomized experiment which maximizes

$$\min_{\phi \, \in \, a(\hat{\theta}_n)} I(\hat{\theta}_n, \phi, E).$$

To discuss this procedure let

$$(33) \qquad I(\theta) = \max_{E} \; \min_{\phi \, \in \, a(\theta)} \; I(\theta, \phi, E)$$

where the maximum is taken with respect to the set of randomized experiments. In [2] it is shown that if there are a finite number of states of nature and a finite number of (nonrandomized) experiments available then as $c \to 0$, the risk or expected cost $R(\theta)$ for using this procedure satisfies

$$(34) \qquad R(\theta) \approx \frac{-c \log c}{I(\theta)}$$

Furthermore this procedure is optimal in the following sense. For a procedure to do

24

better for some θ, i.e., to decrease $R(\theta)$ by some factor for some θ, it must do worse by an order of magnitude for some other θ. In other words suppose that there is another procedure which yields risks $R*(\theta)$, and there is a θ_1 such that

$$\frac{R*(\theta_1)}{R(\theta_1)} \leq e < 1$$

for small c. Then it cannot be the case that $R*(\theta)/R(\theta)$ is bounded away from ∞ for all θ.

6. Miscellaneous remarks.

1. The asymptotic optimality of the procedure of section 5 may not be especially relevant for the initial stages of experimentation, especially if the cost of sampling is not small. At first it is desirable to apply experiments which are informative for a broad range of parameter values. Maximizing the Kullback-Leibler information number may give experiments which are efficient only when θ is close to the estimated value.

2. It is clear that the methods and results apply when the cost of sampling varies from experiment to experiment. Here we are interested in selecting experiments which maximize information per unit cost.

3. Mr. Stuart Bessler has generalized the results of section 5 to cases which involve selecting one of k mutually exclusive hypotheses, and where there are infinitely many experiments available.

4. The asymptotic study of the problem of testing a simple hypothesis versus a simple alternative suggests that it should be possible to refine the stopping rule for the composite problem. While the main term of the risk should not be affected the higher order terms could probably be improved. Such improvement may be quite important in the case where c is not very small. A refinement in the stopping rule would be relevant for problems of testing composite hypotheses even if the problems do not involve the choice of experiments.

5. Mr. A.E. Albert has generalized some of the results of section 5 to the important case where there are infinitely many possible states of nature.

BIBLIOGRAPHY

[1] Blackwell, David and M.A. Girshick, Theory of Games and Statistical Decisions, John Wiley and Sons, New York, 1954.

[2] Chernoff, Herman, "Sequential design of experiments," Ann. Math. Stat, Vol. 30, No. 3, Sept. 1959.

[3] Chernoff, Herman and L. E. Moses, <u>Elementary Decision Theory</u>, John Wiley and Sons, New York, 1959.

[4] Kullback, L. and R. A. Leibler, "On information and sufficiency," Ann. Math. Stat., Vol. 22, No. 1, March 1951, pp. 79-86.

[5] Wald, Abraham, <u>Sequential Analysis</u>, John Wiley and Sons, New York, 1947.

[6] Wald, Abraham and J. Wolfowitz, "Optimum character of the sequential probability ratio test," Ann. Math. Stat., Vol. 19, Sept. 1948, pp. 326-339.

SOME PROBLEMS CONCERNING THE CONSISTENCY OF

MATHEMATICAL MODELS

J. L. Doob

I shall describe this morning various criteria used in adopting a mathematical model of an observed stochastic process. The observed process assigns to certain instants of time t a corresponding number. The number may be the number of cars that have passed some intersection by time t, the number of telephone calls that have been initiated by time t, the insurance payable to accident victims by time t, etc. What kind of mathematical model should one make in such situations?

For example, consider the number of cars that have passed a given point by time t. The first hypothesis is a typical mathematical hypothesis, suggested by the facts and serving to simplify the mathematics. The hypothesis is that the stochastic process of the model has independent increments. That is, if x(t) is the number of cars that have passed by time t, and if $t_1 < \cdots < t_n$, then the random variables $x(t_2) - x(t_1), \ldots,$ $x(t_n) - x(t_{n-1})$ are mutually independent. Roughly, this hypothesis is that future and past traffic are mutually independent.

The next hypothesis, that of stationary increments, states that, if s < t, the distribution of x(t) - x(s) depends only on the time interval length t - s. This hypothesis means that we cannot let time run through both slack and rush hours. Traffic intensity must be constant.

The next hypothesis is that events occur one at a time. This hypothesis is at least natural to a mathematician. Because of limited precision in measurements it means nothing to an observer. (We may, if we wish, define a new kind of event, consisting of simultaneous occurrence of one or more events of the old kind. Then we will have only one of the new kind occurring at any time.)

The next hypothesis is of a more quantitative kind, which also is natural to anyone who has seen Taylor's theorem. It is that the probability that at least one car should pass in a time interval of length h should be ch + o(h). Here c is a positive constant

27

and o(h) means a quantity small compared with h when h is near zero. This hypothesis is usually coupled with the hypothesis, related to one already made on simultaneity, that the probability is o(h) that more than one car passes in a time interval of length h.

We can of course keep adding hypotheses, for example demanding that the number of car passings in an interval of length h have expectation c h. At some stage we would begin to wonder whether all these hypotheses are mutually consistent, and whether some imply the others. In this case it turns out that all of the above conditions are mutually compatible.

Note the different character of the various conditions. The overall one is that a probability model is appropriate. Independence and stationarity of increments are qualitative; the others are quantitative. After imposing such conditions on a mathematical model, possibly unnecessarily many, one must prove that there is a model actually satisfying these conditions. In this particular case there is, the Poisson stochastic process, in which if $s < t$, $x(t) - x(s)$ has a Poisson distribution with mean value a multiple of $t - s$. A great deal of work has been done in this area. The Poisson process arises frequently in this simple form and in more complex forms, in insurance problems and telephone engineering.

A more complex model is obtained by supposing that a system is under investigation which can take on various states numbered 1, 2, ... Define $P_{ij}(t)$ as the probability that if the system is in state i at time r, then it will be in state j at time $r + t$. The form given to this transition probability assumes stationarity, in that there is no dependence on r. Under the further assumption that the conditional probability just described does not change if the states at times prior to r are given (Markov property), the probability relations of the process are determined, up to an assignment of an initial distribution of states. The question now becomes that of the determination of the transition probability functions. The hypothesis that is usually made here is that the probability of a transition from state i to state j in a small time interval, t, has the form (again suggested by Taylor's theorem),

(1) $P_{ij}(t) = t\, q_{ij} + o(t)$, $i \neq j$.

We suppose that the probability of remaining in state i for small time t is near unity, and thus we assume

(2) $P_{ii}(t) = 1 + t\, q_{ii} + o(t),$

where the q_{ij}'s can be evaluated from physical considerations. Obviously $q_{ij} \geq 0$ for $i \neq j$, and $q_{ii} \leq 0$, and the condition $\sum\limits_{j} P_{ij}(t) = 1$ suggests the condition $\sum\limits_{j} q_{ij} = 0$.

The next question is: what kind of model is obtained in this case? If we are given the q_{ij}'s and q_{ii}'s, these tell us the probability, neglecting terms of higher order, of making a specified transition in a small time. Does this imply that given any set of numbers, the q_{ij}'s and q_{ii}'s, we can obtain a unique transition probability matrix system satisfying (1) and (2), or do we have to impose other hypotheses?

If there are only finitely many states it turns out that there is one and only one set of transition probability functions corresponding to the q_{ij} matrix. If we are dealing with a system in which there are infinitely many states, then, (as is known from a good deal of work in the last decade or so), just assigning q_{ij}'s and q_{ii}'s with the obvious relations between them is not enough. We must do more, since if the q_{ii}'s become large as i varies we no longer have a simple case, and encounter many mathematical difficulties. A sufficient condition for uniqueness is that the q_{ii} sequence be bounded.

Consider now an example of a different type, Brownian motion, encountered in many discussions of noise phenomena and molecular and atomic phenomena generally. It is observed that microscopic particles in a fluid undergo spontaneous irregular motion. It was surmised early, and reasonably verified much later, that this motion was due to the impact on the microscopic particle by groups of molecules hitting it on the same side. The particles themselves are so much bigger than the molecules of the fluid, that a molecule hitting a particle would have little effect. But if a "large" number of them happen to hit the particle on the same side, then it will move appreciably, while if they hit on the other side it will move in the opposite direction. Let us see what mathematical model we can construct to describe this physical situation.

Let x(t) be the x coordinate of the moving particle at time t. (If we want to solve the problem in all three dimensions simultaneously we could think of x(t) as a vector). It is not unreasonable as a first approximation to suppose that the x(t) process has independent increments. In this situation, independent increments means that the displacements corresponding to disjoint time intervals are independent, because of the "fact"

29

that the molecules hitting the particle in any one time interval bear no relation to those hitting the particle in any other disjoint time interval. We observe that this hypothesis is plausible if the time intervals are not too close to each other. However the hypothesis of independent increments does not have this latter restriction.

The next hypothesis, more reasonable in this case than in that of the traffic example, is that of stationary increments.

Another natural hypothesis is that the particle trajectories are smooth. Use of the word smooth may bring in ambiguities and therefore it has been subject to many arguments. If we are thinking of these paths as trajectories of particles, then what is meant by smooth is obvious at any particular time. However, some functions which we are at present willing to think of as smooth functions would have been thought of one hundred years ago as functions with very jagged graphs. What we might think of, perhaps, is the minimum hypothesis of smoothness; i.e., that the trajectories are continuous. In other words the particle does not suddenly jump from one position to another.

Going further in the same direction, it might seem reasonable to suppose that the particle trajectories have first and second time derivatives, (that is, that the $x(t)$ sample functions have these derivatives). In physical language this means that the particles have well-defined velocities and accelerations. It has been shown, however, that the hypotheses of stationary independent increments and continuous trajectories suffice to determine the process up to two constant parameters. The displacement $x(t) - x(s)$ is necessarily normally distributed with mean zero and variance proportional to $|t - s|$. This means that it is both unnecessary and risky to make hypotheses about $x'(t)$ and $x''(t)$. In fact, it turns out that in this mathematical model these derivatives do not exist! That is, the sample functions of the $x(t)$ process (we are considering the mathematical model only) are continuous but do not have derivatives.

Here we have reached the case in which our mathematical model has outrun the natural hypotheses. When this was discovered, it was concluded that "anybody could see" that these particles had the most extraordinarily wild oscillations, and so it just looked plausible that the x-coordinate functions of the particles were examples of continuous functions which do not have derivatives. It was then assumed that this was a "real-life" example of degenerate functions that are continuous, but have no derivatives. This was obviously a rationalization, of a type which may be seen frequently in science, even though it does not look like a rationalization until the next stage, when it is shown up for the nonsense it is.

In a later refinement of the mathematical model, due to Ornstein and Uhlenbeck, the hypothesis of independence of increments was dropped, and in this model the sample functions have first (but not second) derivatives. Perhaps scientists had learned the lesson not to take the mathematical model too seriously, for at least now nobody said that you could see by looking at the particles that they had velocities, but did not have accelerations.

The progress from the first to the second model illustrates the fact that no model can hope to reflect all of reality, and extremely delicate properties of the model cannot be taken too literally as direct reflections of reality. The next example also illustrates this.

Consider a simple pendulum. If θ is the angle that the string makes with the vertical,

it turns out, according to the general principles of statistical mechanics, that $\theta(t)$, the value of the angle at time t, is a random variable which is not identically constant even in the absence of external forces. The mean value is 0 and the variance can be computed using the equipartition principle. In the standard mathematical model, $\theta(t)$ has normal distribution, and this means that $\theta(t)$ can take on any value from $-\infty$ to $+\infty$. This can be interpreted to mean that if we wait long enough the pendulum will not only move perceptibly to the naked eye but even go around across the top! This is the kind of delicate result inherent in the model that need not be taken seriously. This is an example that shows that when one constructs a model one may get something more than was bargained for and thereby a limitation on the meaningfulness of the results. One must always distinguish between mathematical and empirical concepts. For example, in the Brownian motion, one cannot talk about the existence of derivatives of the sample functions of the mathematical model. But physical experience and experimentation do not produce mathematical functions, and it is therefore not proper

31

to apply such mathematical words as "continuity" and "derivability" to empirical sample functions.

It is of interest to give some conditions insuring continuity of sample functions, since they are not very well known here, and have appeared in other languages (Russian in particular). From these conditions it will often be possible to draw the proper conclusions concerning certain mathematical models.

The first condition is due to Kolmogorov, who gave it in 1937. What interested him was under what conditions continuous paths were ensured. His condition was simply that there exist $\epsilon > 0$, $\alpha > 0$ such that for $h > 0$ sufficiently small

$$(3) \qquad E \left\{ |x(t+h) - x(t)|^\alpha \right\} \leq const\ h^{1+\epsilon}$$

for all t.

Kolmogorov showed that under these conditions if we have a stochastic process with a given distribution, then the sample functions are continuous, (or at least we can get a model having the same distribution for which the sample functions are continuous).

For example in the Brownian Motion process $x(t+h) - x(t)$ is a normally distributed random variable with mean 0 and variance proportional to h. It can be verified that here (3) is satisfied, and thus the Brownian Motion process has continuous sample functions in the above sense.

Considerably later Čentsov (1956) proved the following result concerning oscillatory discontinuities of sample functions. (Discontinuities can be divided into two types; the type in which there is a limit on each side, called a jump discontinuity, and the other type, the oscillatory discontinuity.) There will be no oscillatory discontinuity if there exist α, β, ϵ, all exceeding zero, such that for h_1, $h_2 > 0$ sufficiently small

$$(4)\quad E \left\{ |x(t) - x(t+h_1)|^\alpha \quad |x(t) - x(t - h_2)|^\beta \right\} \leq const\ (h_1 + h_2)^{1+\epsilon} \quad \text{for all t.}$$

Finally Dobrushin (1958) obtained conditions under which no jumps would be present. His condition is that there should be $\epsilon > 0$ such that

$$(5)\qquad \sup_t P \left\{ |x(t+h) - x(t)| > \epsilon \right\} = o(h)$$

for all h sufficiently small.

It should be noted that there are processes which have jump discontinuities, but no oscillatory ones. For example the Poisson process described at the beginning of the lecture.

32

Suppose we have a process x(t) with the property that

$$E [x(t) \mid x(\tau), \ \tau \leq \tau_o < t] \geq x(\tau_o).$$

For any such processes, which are sometimes called semi-martingales, we know a priori that there are no oscillatory discontinuities. This means that a qualitative hypothesis of this sort will yield at once certain properties of the sample functions. Such broad qualitative assumptions furnish specific properties of the sample functions arising from the model, these being rather delicate properties. We must be careful, as the Brownian Motion example demonstrated, to avoid contradictory assumptions in the mathematical model. This is at least one justification of the mathematician's standard goal of using the fewest possible assumptions. The fewer assumptions the smaller the likelihood of contradictions.

SEQUENTIAL DECISIONING [1]

Merrill M. Flood

Introduction.

Making decisions is hard work. Managers who are faced with too many difficult decisions too fast often suffer physically and mentally. Yet, men who are believed to be capable of making good decisions an unusually high proportion of the time are apt to be well rewarded as executives or leaders. We extoll the traits of coolness and objectivity under stress, and of crisp but considered judgments when time is fleeting. It seems no wonder, in this age of rapid communication and transportation, that managers and scientists are striving to find mathematically rational systems to take over at least some of the load of stressful decision-making in a divided world . Perhaps better decisioning systems of this kind will even improve our mental health as well as our productive efficiency.

No pretense is made here that the mathematical scientists have solved the decision-making problem -- indeed they have barely started on its formulation. However, there is a rapidly growing and impressively solid scientific literature that deals mathematically with various aspects of the familiar problem of choosing well between alternatives [1]. All of this work is lumped here under the ungrammatical name "decisioning science." Our concern will be with a few such concepts and techniques that mathematically minded workers have introduced in recent years.

We are indebted to John von Neumann (1928)[2], for an especially clear insight into the fundamental nature of the problem of making a wise choice among alternatives when there is total uncertainty concerning the likelihood of the possible outcomes. These basic ideas were later expanded by von Neumann (1944), in collaboration with economist

[1] This is a revision of a paper presented at Arden House on June 13, 1956, at the Seventh Annual Industrial Research Conference sponsored by the Department of Industrial and Management Engineering of Columbia University.
The work was supported by the Office of Naval Research, under Contract Nonr - 266(39) with Columbia University.
A rather complete report on the Arden House talk was published by Industrial Laboratories , Vol. 7, September 1956, pp. 50-55.

Oskar Morganstern, to provide a mathematical formulation of the broad problem of social and economic behavior. Their Theory of Games and Economic Behavior[3] is now a classic in the decisioning field, and has provided the main stimulus for the intensive development of mathematical decisioning science since World War II.

We are concerned here with concepts, rather than with mathematical details, and must venture the impossible -- a description of the central concepts of game theory [4] , and of other mathematical decisioning theories, briefly and in reasonably simple non mathematical language. As is typical of the mathematical sciences, any hope of understanding a new concept is very apt to require some understanding of a few older concepts. Here we must assume an adequate understanding of certain older concepts and mathematical systems, such as the calculus of probability, in order to get on with the newer ones -- and do so unblushingly, at the risk of being uncommunicative or even misunderstood. Ample references to fuller treatments are included for those who may wish to explore any of our topics further.

Game Theory and Statistical Decision Theory.

We can illustrate the central idea of game theory by first posing a simple type of management question, and then showing how von Neumann's minimax principle might help to resolve the matter.

Question. How difficult should the first $64,000 question have been made? Situation. The rules are changed slightly from those of the famous $64,000 question television program. The guest is permitted to try to answer the question even if he chooses not to go on for $64,000, and without penalty if he misses, for a bonus prize (cost $4,000 to the sponsor) if he gives the correct answer. He receives only this same prize if he goes on and fails. Data. The sponsor estimates that it will be worth essentially the same to him in advertising value whether or not the guest answers correctly, unless he does go on to try for $64,000. If he does go on, then the sponsor estimates that a winning answer will be equivalent to an increase of $64,000, and a losing answer equivalent to a decrease of $64,000, from the overall advertising value estimated otherwise for the program. The sponsor also has decided that he is totally unable to estimate the odds against the first guest choosing to go on to try the $64,000 question, and that the future of the program will in no way be affected by the difficulty of this first question. Analysis. The net incremental costs to the sponsor, over and beyond those derived from the program independently of this particular decision, may be represented in a four way matrix as follows:

Outcomes

		Answers Correctly	Answers Incorrectly		Costing Matrix	
Choices	Goes on	64 minus 64	4 plus 64	=	0	68
	Stops	32 plus 4	32		36	32

35

Game theory shows how the sponsor can limit himself
to an expected cost amounting to $34,000 simply by tossing a fair coin to
choose between a very easy and a very hard question or, equivalently, by
choosing a question of medium difficulty that he feels the guest is just about
as apt to miss as not. Indeed, if the sponsor uses a question of medium
difficulty it no longer matters to him whether or not the guest chooses to
go on. This is an application of the minimax principle of game theory.

A more general situation would be one in which there were more than two possible

outcomes, but not necessarily the same number of possible choices as there are pos-

sible outcomes. The costing matrix would now show a separate value for each choice-

outcome possibility. The minimax theorem of von Neumann assures us that in the gen-

eral case there always exists at least one set of percentages, with one for each choice

possibility, such that a choice made on the basis of these percentages ensures that

the expected cost will not exceed a certain definite maximum value. Since, on the

other hand, the minimax theory also assures the existence of a set of percentages cor-

responding to the outcome classes that ensures an expected cost at least as great as

this definite maximum value, and an even greater possible cost if the minimax choice

percentages are not used, it seems reasonable to follow the minimax principle. J.D.

Williams gives a useful and amusing set of examples of such "games," with real life

interpretations, in his very readable The Compleat Strategyst [4].

Just in order to show that the von Neumann percentages (Williams calls them "odd-

ments") may not be too easy to calculate for a larger game, but nevertheless do exist,

consider Example 20 from The Compleat Strategyst. This example is concerned with

the problem met by a physician in prescribing one of three medicines for a patient in

the face of uncertainty about which of five strains of bacteria is causing his illness.

The costing matrix entries are the chances that the patient will be relieved by a parti-

cular medicine-strain combination, the medicine to be chosen by the physician and the

strain by "Nature." The costing matrix and minimax percentages are as follows:

Medicine	Strain					
	1	2	3	4	5	
1	0.5	0.5	0.5	0.5	0	0.67
2	1	0	0	0	0	0
3	0	0	0	0	1	0.33
	0	0	0	0.67	0.33	

Physician's Percentages

Nature's Percentages

Under the minimax principle, in this case, the physician would toss a six-sided die

and prescribe medicine 1 if 1, 2, 3 or 4 spots appeared but medicine 3 otherwise. This would ensure odds of 1 to 2 that the patient would be successfully treated, and the physician could not guarantee better odds than these for the patient by any other manner of choosing unless he could somehow obtain further information about the situation.

Sequential Decisioning.

It is apparent in the $64,000 question example that several quite unsatisfactory assumptions were made -- so unsatisfactory, indeed, that it would be perfectly proper to question the usefulness of the entire approach in this case. The example was chosen to serve as a kind of straw man to be attacked in order to bring out some of the conceptual flaws in the game-theoretic model.

> First, it would be very hard to make accurate enough estimates of the true overall worth to the sponsor of the advertising effects under each choice-outcome pair. Unfortunately, this is usually a barrier to the successful use of game theory in practical situations.
> Second, it was a very unrealistic assumption that the reaction to the first program would not affect subsequent results. A common device used in an effort to avoid this difficulty is to solve the problem from the outset for a whole sequence of such programs, but this attempt usually fails because of the extreme computational difficulties encountered as the model is extended in this way.
> Third, it is a little too pessimistic to accept the assumption that Nature will do her expert best to thwart the person making the choice. As Einstein said, Nature seems deep but not malicious.
> Fourth, it is a bit too severe to restrict the available choices definitely and finally to any particular set; there is always at least one other choice, even if it is nothing more than to seek other alternatives before deciding.
> Fifth, there are many other objections that can be raised in connection with the von Neumann game-theoretical model, but they will not be listed here. Suffice it to say that the model is exceedingly suggestive for further work but rarely adequate in a practical situation.

Another kind of formulation for the decisioning problem is typified by the "two-armed bandit problem." One of the many special forms of this problem is as follows:

> A gambler has paid one dollar for the privilege of operating a "two-armed bandit" ten times, and with the right to pull either of the two arms on each successive play. He knows that the machine is so constructed that he will either get no return on any particular play, or will get two dimes back, and that the odds for such success remain constant for each arm during the entire course of ten plays. Finally, he knows that the actual odds for each arm were established independently and in such a way that each possible set of odds is equally likely for an arm. The gambler's problem is to make each successive play in such a way as to maximize his expected total return.

So far as I know, this problem has not yet been solved. Or if it has been solved for two arms and ten plays, it certainly has not been solved for many arms and plays.

Yet, this simple appearing problem has many of the key features of problems that are met in common decisioning situations:

> A sequence of choices is made between alternatives of a fixed set,

each choice leading to an observed success or failure. The underlying mechanism seems unchanging over a long enough period of time so that recent past experiences with it should be a safe guide to future results. How can successive choices best be made?

Herbert Robbins [5] has discussed several variants of the two-armed bandit problem, as a topic in the foundations of science, or of statistical inference, and has remarked that "... the problem represents in a simplified way the general question of how we learn -- or should learn -- from past experience ... ." More recently, Bradt and Karlin [15] have treated certain special cases of the problem.

Several useful techniques for sequential decisioning are now available, although none of them is fully adequate for any substantial class of problems commonly met in industrial management and control situations. Among these are:

1) The Box-Wilson procedure [6] , already successfully used in the field of chemical experimentation.
2) Stochastic approximation procedures, such as the Robbins-Monro [7] and Kiefer-Wolfowitz [8] processes, and generalizations and extensions due to A. Dvoretzky [9] , J.R. Blum [10] , and others [11] .
3) Stochastic game-learning models of the present author [12] , and their psychological counterparts as discussed by Bush-Mosteller [13] and others.
4) The dynamic programming techniques of Richard Bellman [14] and related mathematical programming models.

All of these more recent sequential decisioning models attempt to avoid most of the five basic objections to the von Neumann game-theoretic model that we listed earlier in this paper. Unfortunately, each such attempt has flaws comparable in seriousness to those for game theory. Examples will perhaps best serve to illustrate the kinds of applications considered for some of these recently developed sequential decisioning techniques, and also to show some of their good and bad features. Only the Box- Wilson and Kiefer-Wolfowitz procedures will be discussed here.

Some Sequential Games.

There are a number of interesting and important results pertaining to sequential games. A few of these will be listed here before going on to the sequential decisioning examples. These results indicate the kind of mathematical treatment that is sometimes possible, and for problems that at first formulation seem quite intractable. On the other hand, it is usually surprisingly difficult to extend such results beyond relatively simple special cases.

The theory of games of timing [16] and of games of partitioning [17] has been developed quite extensively during the past ten years. One of the simplest of these games

38

is the "single-shot noisy duel."

> In this duel problem it is supposed that two combatants approach each
> other, starting out of range of each other, with each having the right to
> fire his single-shot weapon at any time during the approach. It is also
> supposed that each knows the other's chances of a hit at each range, that
> a shot can be heard by both, and that if either combatant fires and misses
> then the other will certainly approach close enough to be certain of hitting
> him. The problem is to give a rule for choosing the range at which to fire.
> The answer is essentially that each tries to fire at the first range when
> the sum of their individual probabilities of hitting is unity.

Various generalizations to several-shot cases, including cases where some of the shots

may be silenced, have been posed and solved. The results have found important appli-

cation in armament design for aircraft and other military vehicles. At least one ap-

plication has been made in industry, with regard to the optimal timing of release for

the catalogue of a mail order company. My first contact with this class of problems

was in 1949, when I proposed the single-shot noisy duel model as a possible one to use

in estimating the likely time for an agressor to start a war; in this case, the probabi-

lity of winning the war would be taken as a function of progress in the armament race.

Here, as with other variants of the von Neumann 2-person constant-sum game model,

the difficulties are in choosing realistic values for the payoff functions, while the ma-

thematical determination of the optimal strategies is only computationally difficult.

Another sequential game that has a neat mathematical solution, and one that is some-

what surprising, is one that I shall call the "fiance problem." This may be played as

a 2-person zero-sum parlor game according to the following rules:

> Players A and B start with a perfectly shuffled deck of N cards. The
> cards are numbered from 1 through N on their faces. Player B is re-
> quired to state, on his first move, whether or not the top card is card N.
> He wins the game whenever he says correctly that the top card is card
> N, and he loses whenever he says incorrectly that the top card is card
> N. If he says correctly that the top card is not card N, the Player A
> removes that card, examines the new top card telling Player B whether
> or not it is larger than all cards previously removed, and Player B
> is again required to state whether or not the new top card is card N;
> of course, he says it is not card N if Player A informs him that it is not
> larger than all previous top cards. The problem is to give a rule for
> Player B to use in making his decisions that will maximize his chance for
> winning the game. The (approximate) answer is that he says each of the
> first N/e top cards is not card N, and that the next top card not announced
> as low is card N; his expectation of winning the game is (approximately)
> 1/e if he uses this decision rule. (The exact formulas for the decision rule,
> and for the chance of winning, are quite easily derived.)

A sequential decisioning problem that I posed in 1950, as the "fiancé problem," is the

following:

> A young girl wishes to marry the finest young man she can find. She
> has met several young men, and some of them have asked for her hand

in marriage. How can she best decide whether to marry one of the men she already knows or to continue her search for a still better husband?

This problem was posed in order to show the importance of the restriction, in the game theory model, to a known set of alternatives -- whereas the critical decision is instead often that relating to alternatives unknown and even unsuspected. Or, in general, the usual practical problem is to decide whether to act on the basis of information presently available about explicitly recognized alternatives or to search and reflect in the hope of discovering substantially better alternatives.

If we grant that the mathematical fiance problem is not a perfectly valid representation of the young girl's problem, and such mathematical models are never completely faithful representations, we can nevertheless get some help from the mathematical solution as to the type of rule the young girl might best use. And in other problems, where the mathematical model is more valid, the solution may give important help; for example, in selecting the best item in a sample when destructive measurements must be made to determine the precise quality of each item even though an item may be compared to all its predecessors, the mathematical solution to the fiancé problem would give a precise answer. Here again, there are real difficulties in making the model sufficiently realistic while the mathematical solution is only computationally troublesome. Other examples of applications are to be found where the passing of time, or the forgetting of information, plays the role of passing over top cards, yet with the capability of deciding whether the current case is or is not better than all previous experienced and in situations where the total number of possible cases is known precisely.

Another kind of sequential game, and the one of greatest interest here, is typified by the "explorer's problem":

> An explorer is searching for the point of greatest thickness of ice in a given polar region. He measures thickness by test borings, each of which costs him the same amount. Each inch of added depth discovered has a known value to him. His problem is to make a sequence of test borings, stopping when he believes that further exploration would not be apt to yield him further gain.

There is no ready answer to this problem, although several recent results in sequential decision theory are useful in planning an exploration of this kind. More generally, this type of problem assumes that there is some real but unknown pattern to the surface being explored and the need is for some systematic way of searching so as to take some advantage of this lack of randomness in depths over the region being explored. Furthermore, each measurement is subject to error so that several observations at any one point may differ appreciably from one another. An essential feature is that successive observations bear a cost that must be deducted from the over-all value of the completed task. Although there is some similarity between the explorer's problem and the fiance problem, they differ critically in that patterning was assumed not to exist in the fiance problem.

The explorer's problem is the common one met by a design engineer. For example, if the problem is to design a chemical refinery then values of various parameters, such as sizes, pressures, and temperatures, must be chosen by the designer over the region allowed so as to optimize expected yield of the refinery. A calculation of expected yield for any one set of design values bears a cost, and the designer must do a sequence of such computations (or trials) in his attempt to get a good design without too great design costs. Here the design parameters, perhaps in many dimensions, are analogous to the two geographical coordinates in the explorer's problem. Some examples of this kind of sequential search problem will now be considered in more detail.

The Alcohol Plant - An Example.

D. S. McArthur [18] has constructed a simple analog computer to serve as an abstract representation of some of the more interesting decision-making problems encountered by the manager of a refinery. He has called this computer the "Alcohol Plant," and he has conducted some very interesting experiments with it in his investigation of the decision-making procedures that are used or that might well be used by plant managers.

The Alcohol Plant has five process parameters, represented by settings on five dials, and a yield variable represented by a pointer reading on a voltmeter. There is also a dial, to be set by the experimenter, that introduces statistical variation into the yields. An experimental run consists in a series of parameter settings by a manager, serving as experimental subject, after each of which the experimenter reports the yield after introducing appropriate statistical variation. The objective of the manager is to find a set of five parameter values that produces high yield, and he is to discover the settings he prefers by making his sequence of trials in such a way that he

41

rapidly discovers a good set of parameter values.

Under the rules used by McArthur, the subject is charged roughly one unit for each yield observation in his sequence and he is credited with four units for each point gained in yield over 24. The manager is told, before the experimental run, that:

1) The average yield is exactly 24 if each process dial is set at 50,
2) The statistical variation is represented by a normal distribution with mean value 0, and standard deviation 2.5, for any particular setting of the process dials,
3) There is a unique setting for the process dials that produces the greatest possible average yield.
4) Each process dial may be set anywhere between 0 and 85 on its scale, and the maximum possible average yield is less than 50, and
5) The functional relationships between yield and process parameters is continuous, in the technical mathematical sense.

It can be seen immediately that no more than 100 observations can possibly be taken with profit, since 25 points is about the maximum possible gain in yield but worth only 100 as contrasted with a charge of 100. These rules certainly seem to represent one kind of sequential decisioning problem met by process managers, and one where there is no positive assurance of eventual gain from even the wisest possible choice of experimental program.

The mathematical decisioning technique that might at first seem most suitable for this kind of problem is the Box-Wilson procedure [6] . In very rough terms, this procedure requires that a few sets of parameter values be tried, and the resulting yields observed, where the trial sets are arranged in a systematic manner about some particular central set. A sort of topographical contour map is then made to fit these observed yields as well as possible, and the resulting contours suggest the direction in which to change the parameter values so as to take the steepest path toward the summit sought. This method can be visualized in three dimensions as an ordinary contour map in which the two ground-position coordinates correspond to two process parameter values and a map elevation corresponds to the average process yield resulting. Unfortunately, when there are even as many as five process parameters, the topographical complexities possible are so great that the Box-Wilson procedure may very easily require a great number of successive recalculations before the summit is neared -- and there is also no way of knowing whether or not the actual summit is or is not very much higher than the best yield observed at any particular stage of the calculation.

42

A simple single-parameter example may help to illustrate some of the difficulties encountered in problems like that posed by McArthur for the Alcohol Plant. Suppose that the average yield y and a parameter x are connected functionally by the relation

$$y = \frac{x^5}{5} - \frac{10x^4}{4} + \frac{35x^3}{3} - \frac{50x^2}{2} + 24x$$

A problem of the kind we are considering requires finding the value of x between zero and five that yields the largest value for y. This would be a very simple problem in the differential calculus if we in fact knew the algebraic relationship between x and y; however, in our problem, we can find the yield y corresponding to a given parameter value x only by conducting an experiment that provides an estimate of y that is subject to some error. For example, if the value x = 1 were tried several times we would observe values for y clustered about y = 8.3667; the spread of the cluster about this true average value would depend upon the amount of random variation in the process.

The graph of our function is shown roughly in <u>Figure 1</u>.

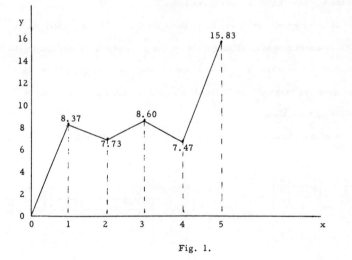

Fig. 1.

The best average yield is obtained when x = 5. If one used the Box-Wilson procedure, with the erroneous conviction that there was a unique "peak," then the parameter value x = 1 would very likely be selected eventually if the initial central point was a value of x less than two, and the summit at x = 5 would be selected only if the initial central point was a value of x not less than four. Of course, an expert with the Box-Wilson

43

procedure takes precautions against making erroneous assumptions but there is no certain way to avoid all of these dangers -- and the chances for making such errors increase rapidly as the number of parameters grows larger.

Another example, this time one with two parameters and superimposed error in yield, will help to show the characteristics of the more general sequential search problem -- as met in the Alcohol Plant, for example. We will call the parameters U and V, and the yield F, with the following conditions:

1) The parameters U and V are expressed in percentage units;
2) It is known that there is a unique pair of values for U and V that produces the maximum average yield F, and that this maximum yield is expressed in percentage units;
3) The yield F is a continuous and finite function of the two parameters;
4) The cost of one observation on F is one-fourth the value of a percentage point in yield.

Our problem, exactly similar to that for the Alcohol Plant, is to maximize net value, where net value is the difference between four times the true average yield corresponding to the pair of parameter values finally selected as a result of the experimental analysis and the number of trial observations taken.

Since there is no especially good way in which to solve this kind of problem, and since our main interest now is in gaining a feeling for such problems, we shall proceed in a crude, common-sense sort of way -- while making some use of "steepest ascent" techniques like those of Box-Wilson. We gamble with a start on 25 points, and obtain the following yield data:

Yields Without Error
(from Figure 2.)

V \ U	0	25	50	75	100
0	9	18	18	28	72
25	23	56	17	50	33
50	21	35	11	15	23
75	14	7	24	51	8
100	47	11	19	9	13

Yields With Error
($\sigma = 5$)

V \ U	0	25	50	75	100
0	8	15	17	22	75
25	10	58	17	64	36
50	23	33	20	17	27
75	16	4	22	52	4
100	56	7	17	7	18

From this initial sample it would appear that the parameter pair (100, 0), with an observed yield of 75, might be in a region worth further exploration. But before we do go on it will be worthwhile to examine our present situation a bit further.

If there were no error in the yield measurements, then we could stop and be assured of a net value of (4 x 75 - 25 = 275). Furthermore, since maximum yield is certainly

44

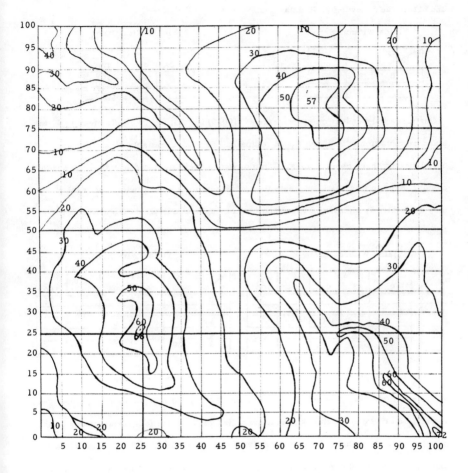

Fig. 2

not greater than 100, we could not take as many as 100 more observations without certain loss; for example, also, if 25 more observations were taken the yield obtained would have to be above 81 for a profit. But there is error in the yield measurements, and of an amount as yet unknown, so there is no assurance that 75 is the actual average yield. Again, on a common sense basis, we take five observations near (100, 0) and obtain the following yield data:

Yields Without Error

U V	90	100
0	38	72
10	62	39

Yields With Error

U V	90	100
0	40	{69 {70
10	63	35

Our three independent measurements at (100, 0) are 75, 69, 70; their mean is 72 and standard deviation is 3.3, but these estimates are quite unreliable since they are based on only three observations. Common sense, perhaps aided by experience with contour maps in this case, suggests that pairs summing to 100, with U at least 90, may be relatively high in the region now under exploration; yields from five of these follow.

Yields Without Error

U V	92	94	96	98	100
0					72
2				69	
4	.		60		
6		60			
8	60				

Yields With Error

U V	92	94	96	98	100
0					71
2				60	
4			61		
6		59			
8	69				

Logical contouring of all our data would suggest a rather high "ridge" represented by the parameter pairs where U + V = 100 and U ≥ 90, but now the pair (92, 8) has given a yield of 69 comparable with that averaging 71.1 for the four observations on the pair (100, 0). Our single observation at (92, 8) has given us a much less reliable estimate than our four observations at (100, 0), the latter with an estimated mean of 71.1 and estimated standard deviation of 2.6. Clearly, we need some more methodical way in which to make our final choice even if we gamble on the best possible choice being in the general region now under exploration, and there is absolutely no assurance that distinctly better yields are not available near (25, 25) or at some other pair not yet tried.

The Box-Wilson procedure is indeed of some help once we commit ourselves to the assumption that there is a unique "peak" within the region under exploration, in this case where $90 \leqslant U \leqslant 100$ and $0 \leqslant V \leqslant 10$. This is accomplished by fitting a second degree polynomial in the variables U and V to the available data, by the method of least squares, and then calculating mathematically the pair of values for U and V that gives the greatest value for this polynomial over the allowable ranges for U and V. We shall not here discuss the many simplifying techniques for carrying out such a polynomial fitting computation, and we shall also not discuss the very important matter of proper selection of the pairs to be used in obtaining observations on yields; we shall be concerned only with the general concepts.

In principle then, we need to find values for the coefficients of a polynomial

$$P(U, V) = AU^2 + BUV + CV^2 + DU + EV + F$$

that passes closest, in the least squares sense, to our observed yields. Since we have observed on only 11 pairs and need to estimate six coefficients, our fitted polynomial is not too firmly determined; in practice we would also not repeat observations for one pair, as we have done here four times at $(100, 0)$. Although this calculation has not been made for this case, it seems likely that it would in fact give as answer a pair close to $(100, 0)$. It also happens that this problem, as set up, has the highest peak at $(100, 0)$ where the average yield is 72.

In the case of the Alcohol Plant, which has five parameters, it could not possibly be profitable to start by trying even three values for each parameter, since this would be a total of $3^5 = 729$ pairs and at most 100 observations can possibly be taken with profit. Even trying all the extreme pairs, with two values per parameter, would require $2^5 = 32$ pairs.

Our examples have shown how very formidable are problems of this kind, even with a few parameters; yet managers and engineers are constantly making decisions of just this kind, and apparently with considerable skill.

Sequential Decisioning Formulas.

There are several recent papers [11] on "stochastic approximation" that give very interesting mathematical procedures for solving the kind of sequential decisioning problems we have been considering. Unfortunately, each of these procedures is quite limited in its scope of application. One of them, the Kiefer-Wolfowitz procedure [8],

47

will be discussed briefly here as an example of this general approach. We shall here consider only the single parameter case, and for that only one of an infinite number of the applicable Kiefer-Wolfowitz procedures.

Our example is similar to the one used earlier, where yield Y and parameter X are connected by the broken line relation shown in Figure 3.

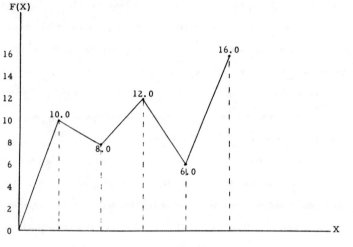

Fig. 3

Now, however, we shall superimpose an error in such a way that the observed value of Y will be Y + E, where E is normally distributed with mean zero and standard deviation unity.

In application of the Kiefer-Wolfowitz procedure to this problem:

1) Choose a value X_1 arbitrarily, such that $0 \leqslant X_1 \leqslant 5$;

2) Take yield observations for the parameter values $(X_1 + 1)$ and $(X_1 - 1)$, and call these G_1 and H_1;

3) Calculate a value $X_2 = X_1 + (G_1 - H_1)$;

4) Take yield observations for the parameter values $\left(X_2 + \dfrac{1}{\sqrt[3]{2}} \right)$ and $\left(X_2 - \dfrac{1}{\sqrt[3]{2}} \right)$, call these G_2 and H_2.

5) Calculate a value $X_3 = X_2 + \dfrac{(G_2 - H_2)}{\sqrt[3]{4}}$;

6) Continue this process, getting observations G_n and H_n for $\left(X_n + \dfrac{1}{\sqrt[3]{n}} \right)$ and $\left(X_n - \dfrac{1}{\sqrt[3]{n}} \right)$ where $X_{n+1} = X_n + \dfrac{(G_n - H_n) \sqrt[3]{n}}{n}$.

48

Table 1

n	X_n	$\dfrac{1}{\sqrt[3]{n}}$	$F(X_n + \frac{1}{\sqrt[3]{n}})$	$F(X_n - \frac{1}{\sqrt[3]{n}})$	E_G	E_H	G_n	H_n
1	0.25	1.00	9.5	0	-0.28	-0.56	9.22	0.00
2	5.00	0.79	16.0	8.1	-0.26	-1.11	15.74	6.99
3	5.00	0.69	16.0	9.1	0.64	-2.57	16.64	6.53
4	5.00	0.63	16.0	9.7	0.37	0.03	16.37	9.73
5	5.00	0.58	16.0	10.2	2.75	0.56	18.75	10.76
6	5.00	0.55	16.0	10.5				
		e t c .						
50	5.00	0.27	16.0	13.3	0.39	-0.44	16.39	12.86
		e t c .						
100	5.00	0.22	16.0	13.8	-3.00	0.00	13.00	13.80
101	4.96	0.21	16.0	13.5	0.00	0.00	16.00	13.50
102	5.00							
		e t c .						
1000	5.00	0.10	16.0	15.0	-3.00	0.00	13.00	15.00
1001	4.98	0.10	16.0	14.8	0.00	0.00	16.00	14.80
1002	4.99	e t c .						
/	/	/	/	/	/	/	/	/
1	2.50	1.00	9.00	9.00	-0.28	-0.56	8.72	8.44
2	2.78	0.79	10.28	8.02	-0.26	-1.11	10.02	6.91
3	4.02	0.69	13.10	10.00	0.64	-2.57	13.74	7.43
4	5.00	e t c .						
/	/	/	/	/	/	/	/	/
1	3.00	1.00	6.00	8.00	-0.28	-0.56	5.72	7.44
2	1.72	0.79	10.02	9.30	-0.26	-1.11	9.76	8.19
3	2.35	0.69	11.76	8.68	0.64	-2.57	12.40	6.11
4	3.79	0.63	10.20	11.04	0.37	0.03	10.57	11.07

Since we have limited X_n to the closed interval (0, 5), we shall arbitrarily change any negative argument in F(X) to zero, for the next step, and limit positive arguments to five should a larger value ever be given by the formula. A sample computation for our example is shown in Table 1.

Although this sample calculation proves nothing, it does illustrate the manner in which the Kiefer-Wolfowitz procedure tends eventually to select the value X = 5, and then tends to stay there. It also illustrates the lack of tendency to stay at the second highest peak, located at X = 3 in this case.

There are several ways in which currently available stochastic approximation procedures, such as the one of Kiefer-Wolfowitz, are not satisfactory:

> 1) They depend upon the important restriction against multiple peaks, and upon other less severe but essential restrictions concerning the nature of the functional relationships between yield and parameters, even for assurance that the sequential search would ultimately settle down upon the desired parameter values;
> 2) They may settle down too slowly to be of use, and the settling rate depends in a critical and unknown manner upon certain constants that must be chosen to establish a specific procedure;
> 3) They include no "stop rule," that indicates when the calculation should be terminated if there is a cost of some kind associated with each additional step.

There are several features of this type of procedure that make them especially attractive:

> 4) They are "adaptive," in the sense that continued application over time after some unsuspected change has occurred in the underlying relationship between yield and parameters will automatically shift to the proper parameter values;
> 5) They require the same simple calculation after each observation, and do not require the retention of old data for use in future calculations;
> 6) They are reasonably self-corrective with respect to computational errors, since such errors have the same kind of effects as do other errors comprising the underlying system.

For all these reasons, the stochastic approximation procedures would seem to have their most promising applications in systems where successive observations are frequent, where the underlying functional relationship is changing occasionally and at unsuspected times, and where profits are heavily dependent upon making appropriate corrections regularly during the operation of the system.

Summary.

There is under development a set of new mathematical decisioning procedures that show great promise for effective application in managing and controlling systems where the selection of best current operating conditions is redetermined continuously on the basis of past results. These procedures may be used effectively from the start of operation of a system, and their suitability in any particular instance depends only upon knowing that the system meets certain broad conditions imposed by a few rather unrestrictive mathematical conditions. The present paper offers a few illustrative examples of these newer procedures, and makes some comparisons between them and certain other decisioning techniques based on the minimax approach of game theory.

BIBLIOGRAPHY

[1] Flood, Merrill M., "Decision Making -- Symposium: Management Science Today & Tomorrow," Management Science, Vol. 1, No. 2, January 1955, pp. 167-169.

[2] von Neumann, J., "Zur Theorie der Gesellschaftsspiele," Mathmatische Annalen, Vol. 100, 1928, pp. 295-320.

[3] von Neumann, J., and Morgenstern, Oskar, Theory of Games and Economic Behavior, Princeton, 1944.

[4] Williams, J.D., The Compleat Strategyst. New York, McGraw Hill Book Co., Inc., 1954.

[5] Robbins, Herbert, "Some Aspects of the Sequential Design of Experiments," Bull. Amer. Math. Soc., Vol. 58, No. 5, pp. 527-535.

[6a] Davies, O.L., The Design and Analysis of Industrial Experiments, Oliver & Boyd, England, and Hafner, New York, 1954.

[6b] Hunter, John S., "Searching for Optimum Conditions," Transactions of the New York Academy of Sciences, Ser. II, Vol. 17, No. 2, December 1954, pp. 124-132.

[7] Robbins, H., and Monro, S., "A Stochastic Approximation Method," Ann. Math. Stat., Vol. 22, 1951, pp. 400-407.

[8] Kiefer, J., and Wolfowitz, J., "Stochastic Estimation of the Maximum of a Regression Function," Ann. Math. Stat., Vol. 23, 1952, pp. 462-466.

[9] Dvoretzky, A., "On Stochastic Approximation," Proceedings of the Third Berkeley Symposium on Mathematical Statistics and Probability, University of California Press, Berkeley, 1956.

[10] Blum, J.R., "Multidimensional Stochastic Approximation Methods," Ann. Math. Stat., Vol. 25, 1954, pp. 737-744.

[11] Derman, Cyrus, Stochastic Approximation. Paper read before the Institute of Mathematical Statistics, December 29, 1955, New York.

[12] Flood, Merrill M., "Game-Learning Theory and Some Decision-Making Experiments," Decision Processes, Thrall, Coombs, & Davis (Editors). New York, John Wiley & Co., 1954, pp. 139-158.

[13] Bush, R.R., and Mosteller, C.F., Stochastic Models for Learning. John Wiley & Sons, Inc., New York, 1955.

[14] Bellman, Richard, "Dynamic Programming," Princeton University Press, Princeton, 1957.

[15a] Bradt, R.N., and Samuel Karlin, "On the Design and Comparison of Certain Dichotomous Experiments," Ann. Math. Stat., Vol. 27, No. 2, June 1956, pp. 390-409.

[15b] Bradt, R.N., S.M. Johnson, and Samuel Karlin, "On Sequential Designs for Maximizing the Sum of n Observations," Ann. Math. Stat., Vol. 27, No. 4, December 1956, pp. 1060-1074.

[16] Shiffman, Max, "Games of Timing." In: Kuhn, H.W., and A.W. Tucker (Editors), Contributions to the Theory of Games, II, Annals of Mathematics Studies 28, Princeton University Press, Princeton, 1953, pp. 97-123.

[17] Luce, R.D., and Howard Raiffa, Games and Decisions, John Wiley & Sons, Inc., New York, 1957.

[18] McArthur, D.S., Unpublished. Esso Research and Engineering Company. I am greatly indebted to Dr. McArthur for discussion of his work with the Alcohol Plant, and for the opportunity to conduct experiments using this computer.

LOWER BOUNDS FOR THE EXPECTED SAMPLE SIZE OF A SEQUENTIAL TEST[1]

Wassily Hoeffding

Summary. This expository paper is concerned with lower bounds for the expected sample size $E_o(N)$ of an arbitrary sequential test whose error probabilities at two parameter points θ_1 and θ_2 do not exceed given numbers α_1 and α_2, where $E_o(N)$ is evaluated at a third parameter point θ_o. The bounds in (1.3) and (1.4) are shown to be attainable or nearly attainable in certain cases where θ_o lies between θ_1 and θ_2.

1. Introduction and main results. Let $X_1, X_2, \ldots$ be a sequence of independent random variables having a common probability density f. (All results also apply to the case where the distribution of X_i is discrete and f(x) denotes the probability of $X_i = x$; in this case the integrals in the formulas are to be replaced by sums.) One of two decisions, d_1 and d_2, is to be made. Let f_1 and f_2 be two probability densities such that decision $d_2(d_1)$ is considered as wrong if $f = f_1(f_2)$. We shall consider sequential tests (decision rules) for making decision d_1 or d_2, such that the probability of a wrong decision does not exceed a positive number α_i when $f = f_i$ (i = 1, 2). Let N denote the (random) number of observations required by such a test. This paper is concerned with lower bounds for $E_o(N)$, the expected sample size when $f = f_o$, where f_o is in general different from f_1 and f_2.

The background of this problem is as follows. Suppose that f depends on a real parameter θ and f_i corresponds to the value θ_i, where $\theta_1 < \theta_2$. Suppose further that decision d_1 or d_2 is preferred according as $\theta \leq \theta_1$ or $\theta \geq \theta_2$, and that neither decision is strongly preferred if $\theta_1 < \theta < \theta_2$. If we require that the probability of a wrong decision does not exceed $\alpha_1(\alpha_2)$ if $\theta \leq \theta_1(\theta \geq \theta_2)$, the condition of the preceding paragraph will be satisfied. For a number of the common one-parameter families of distributions (such as the normal distributions with mean θ and known variance or with

---

[1] This research was partially supported by the United States Air Force through the Air Force Office of Scientific Research of the Air Research and Development Command, under Contract No. AF 49(638)-261. Reproduction in whole or in part is permitted for any purpose of the United States Government. Part of this work was done while the author was a visiting professor at Stanford University.

variance θ and known mean, or binomial distributions with mean θ) Wald's sequential probability ratio (SPR) test for testing the hypothesis $\theta = \theta_1$ against the alternative $\theta = \theta_2$ can be applied to this problem.

The SPR test can be defined as follows [8]. Let a and b be two constants such that $b < 0 < a$. If $x_1, x_2, \ldots, x_n$ are the first n observations $(n \geq 1)$ and Z_n denotes the sum

$$\log \frac{f_2(x_1)}{f_1(x_1)} + \log \frac{f_2(x_2)}{f_1(x_2)} + \cdots + \log \frac{f_2(x_n)}{f_1(x_n)}$$

sampling is continued as long as $b < Z_n < a$. Sampling is stopped as soon as one of these inequalities is violated and according as $Z_n \leq b$ or $Z_n \geq a$, decision d_1 or d_2 is made. It is known [10] that the SPR test for testing θ_1 against θ_2, with error probabilities equal to α_1 and α_2, minimizes the expected sample size at these two parameter values. In typical cases its expected sample size is largest when θ is between θ_1 and θ_2, (that is, when neither decision is strongly preferred), and in general there exist tests whose expected sample size at these intermediate θ values is smaller than that of the SPR test. (A special case in which a SPR test minimizes the maximum expected sample size will be discussed in section 2.)

In principle it is possible to construct a test which minimizes the expected sample size at an arbitrary θ value or minimizes the maximum expected sample size. Kiefer and Weiss [5] have proved important qualitative properties of such tests. They have shown that for one-parameter families such as those mentioned above, a test which minimizes the expected sample size at a value θ with $\theta_1 < \theta < \theta_2$ can be defined in terms of two finite sequences of numbers, $a_1, a_2, \ldots, a_M$ and $b_1, b_2, \ldots, b_M$, such that $a_{n-1} \geq a_n$, $b_{n-1} \leq b_n$, $b_n \leq a_n$ for $n \leq M$ and $b_M = a_M$. Sampling is continued as long as $b_n < Z_n < a_n$ and is stopped as soon as $Z_n \leq b_n$ or $Z_n \geq a_n$, and decision $d_1(d_2)$ is made in the first (second) case. Thus the test requires at most M observations.

The actual determination of the numbers a_n and b_n and the evaluation of the expected sample size and the error probabilities meets with difficulties which have not been overcome so far. Therefore attempts have been made to find a test which, without actually minimizing the maximum expected sample size, comes close to this goal, or at least substantially improves upon the performance of known tests. I mention in particular the work of Donnelly [2] and Anderson [1] who, independently of each other,

54

considered tests like those just described, with $a_n = c_1 + d_1 n$ and $b_n = c_2 + d_2 n$, where $c_1 > 0 > d_1$ and $c_2 < 0 < d_2$. (Anderson also considered truncated tests of this type.) Thus if the successive values of $Z = Z_n$ ($n = 1, 2, \ldots$) are plotted in the (n, Z) plane, the boundaries at which the SPR test stops are two parallel lines, the boundaries for a Kiefer-Weiss test are monotone curves, the upper decreasing and the lower increasing, and the boundaries for a Donnelly-Anderson test are converging straight lines.

The performance of these and other tests can, to some extent, be judged by comparing, at any parameter point θ, the expected sample size of the test with the smallest expected sample size attainable by any test having the same error probabilities at θ_1 and θ_2. In the ignorance of the minimum expected sample size, the comparison may be made with a lower bound for this minimum. If the discrepancy is small, both the test (as judged by this criterion) and the bound cannot be greatly improved. Our main concern will be with bounds which are best when θ is between θ_1 and θ_2.

We admit arbitrary (in general, randomized) sequential tests which terminate with probability one under each of f_0, f_1, and f_2. We also assume with no loss of generality that $E_0(N) < \infty$. To exclude trivialities we suppose that $\alpha_1 + \alpha_2 < 1$.

The first lower bound for the expected sample size was given by Wald (see [8], p. 197) who proved for the case $f_0 = f_1$ that

$$(1.1) \quad E_1(N) \geq \frac{\alpha_1 \log \frac{\alpha_1}{1 - \alpha_2} + (1 - \alpha_1) \log \frac{1 - \alpha_1}{\alpha_2}}{\int f_1 \, [\, \log(f_1/f_2) \,] \, dx}$$

and an analogous inequality for $f_0 = f_2$. (Wald's proof assumes a non-randomized test, but this restriction is easy to remove.) It can be shown that both the numerator and the denominator in (1.1) are positive; the integral in the denominator can be equal to $+ \infty$, in which case the lower bound has the trivial value 0. The sign of equality in (1.1) can be attained with a SPR test in the case where the ratio f_1/f_2 takes on the two values C and $1/C$ only, provided that the values α_1 and α_2 can be achieved as error probabilities in this test. In certain other cases the sign of equality can be nearly attained with a SPR test.

An extension of (1.1) to the case of an arbitrary f_0 has been given by the author [3]:

$$(1.2) \quad E_0(N) \geq \sup_{0 < c < 1} \frac{- \log[\, \alpha_1^c (1 - \alpha_2)^{1-c} + (1 - \alpha_1)^c \alpha_2^{1-c} \,]}{c \int f_0 \, (\log \frac{f_0}{f_1}) \, dx + (1-c) \int f_0 \, (\log \frac{f_0}{f_2}) \, dx}$$

55

For $f_0 = f_1$ and $c \to 1$, (1.2) reduces to (1.1). This bound is likely to be close when f_0 is close to f_1 or f_2.

In this paper two new inequalities will be considered,

$$(1.3) \qquad E_0(N) \geq \frac{1 - \alpha_1 - \alpha_2}{1 - \int \min(f_0, f_1, f_2)dx}$$

and

$$(1.4) \qquad E_0(N) \geq \frac{\{[(\tau/4)^2 - \zeta \log(\alpha_1 + \alpha_2)]^{1/2} - \tau/4\}^2}{\zeta^2}$$

where

$$(1.5) \qquad \zeta = \max(\zeta_1, \zeta_2), \quad \zeta_i = \int f_0(\log \frac{f_0}{f_i})dx, \quad i = 1, 2,$$

and

$$(1.6) \qquad \tau^2 = \int (\log \frac{f_2}{f_1} - \zeta_1 + \zeta_2)^2 f_0 \, dx.$$

Note that $\zeta_i \geq 0$, the strict inequality applying whenever f_0 and f_i are densities of different distributions.

In the proof of (1.4) it is assumed that, in addition to the existence of the integrals in (1.5) and (1.6),

$$(1.7) \qquad f_0(x) = 0 \text{ implies } \min[f_1(x), f_2(x)] = 0,$$

and that the equation

$$(1.8) \qquad E_0 \left(\sum_{j=1}^{N} Y_j \right)^2 = \tau^2 E_0(N)$$

is satisfied, where

$$(1.9) \qquad Y_j = \log \frac{f_2(X_j)}{f_1(X_j)} - \zeta_1 + \zeta_2.$$

Concerning the last assumption we note that $\zeta_1 - \zeta_2 = \int f_0 [\log(f_2/f_1)] \, dx$, so that $E_0(Y_j) = 0$ and, by (1.6), $E_0(Y_j^2) = \tau^2$. Equation (1.8) has been proved by Wald [7] and Wolfowitz [11] under certain conditions; see also Seitz and Winkelbauer [6]. It certainly holds if N is bounded or if $Y_1 + \cdots + Y_m$ is bounded for m < N. It is clear that if condition (1.8) is satisfied for a test which minimizes $E_0(N)$, then inequality (1.4) is true also for any other test. In particular this is true under the assumptions of Theorem 4 of Kiefer and Weiss [5], which imply that if a test minimizes $E_0(N)$, then N is bounded.

Inequalities (1.3) and (1.4) will be discussed in the following sections. Proofs of the inequalities are given in [4] .

2. Discussion of inequality (1.3). The sign of equality in (1.3) can be attained in two cases, in both of which

$$(2.1) \qquad f_o(x) \geq \min [\, f_1(x), \, f_2(x) \,] \; .$$

(This condition is satisfied for many common one-parameter families of distributions when θ_o is between θ_1 and θ_2). Under condition (2.1) inequality (1.3) can be written as

$$(2.2) \qquad E_o(N) \geq \frac{1 - \alpha_1 - \alpha_2}{1 - \int \min (f_1, f_2) dx} = \frac{1 - \alpha_1 - \alpha_2}{\frac{1}{2} \int |f_1 - f_2| \; dx} \; .$$

The last equation is obtained by integrating on both sides of the identity

$$\frac{1}{2}(f_1 + f_2) - \min (f_1, f_2) = \frac{1}{2} |f_1 - f_2| \; .$$

In the first case where equality in (2.2) can be attained, the densities f_i are arbitrary, subject only to (2.1), but the values α_1 and α_2 are severely restricted by the condition that they be attainable as error probabilities by a test which uses at most one observation, x_1, and decision $d_1 (d_2)$ is made if $f_1(x_1) - f_2(x_1)$ is positive (negative). ("At most" means that we may decide at random, with prescribed probabilities, between taking no or one observation, and in the former case choose at random d_1 or d_2.)

The second case in which equality can be attained in (2.2) is where, in addition to (2.1), the three densities $f_o(x)$, $f_1(x)$, and $f_2(x)$ are equal to each other on a set of points having a positive probability. In particular, let $f_i(x)$ be the rectangular density which is equal to $1/L$ if $\theta_i - L/2 \leq x \leq \theta_i + L/2$ and zero elsewhere, and let $0 < \theta_2 - \theta_1 < L$, $\theta_1 \leq \theta_o \leq \theta_2$. Choose two numbers c and d such that $\theta_2 - L/2 \leq c < d \leq \theta_1 + L/2$, and consider the following test. Sampling is continued as long as the observations $x_1, x_2, \ldots$ fall into the interval (c, d). Sampling is stopped as soon as $x_n \leq c$ or $x_n \geq d$, and decision $d_1 (d_2)$ is made if $x_n \leq c (x_n \geq d)$. It can be calculated that in this case the error probabilities are

$$\alpha_1 = \frac{\theta_1 - d + (L/2)}{L - d + c} \quad , \quad \alpha_2 = \frac{c - \theta_2 + (L/2)}{L - d + c} \; .$$

Also

$$1 - \int \min (f_1, f_2) dx = \frac{\theta_2 - \theta_1}{L}$$

57

and

$$E_o(N) = \frac{L}{L - d + c}$$

Hence the two sides of inequality (2.2) are equal. In this example equality in (2.2) can be achieved for any values α_1 and α_2 such that $\alpha_1 \geq 0$, $\alpha_2 \geq 0$, and $\alpha_1 + \alpha_2 \leq 1$, either by a suitable choice of c and d in the test just described, or by a test using at most one observation. Moreover, the expected sample size of the test here considered, assuming that the distribution of x_i is rectangular on an interval of length L with an arbitrary mean θ, can be shown to attain its maximum when $\theta_1 \leq \theta \leq \theta_2$. Hence the test minimizes the maximum expected sample size.

The present test is a modified version of Wald's SPR test. To see this, let f_{in} stand for $f_i(x_1)f_i(x_2) \cdots f_i(x_n)$, and let $0 < B \leq A$. The SPR test for testing f_1 against f_2, is defined in [9] as follows. (The definition differs slightly from that in [8] .) Sampling is continued as long as $B < f_{2n}/f_{1n} < A$. If one of these inequalities is violated, one proceeds as follows. If $f_{2n}/f_{1n} < B$, hypothesis f_1 is accepted. If $f_{2n}/f_{1n} > A$, hypothesis f_2 is accepted. In the case $B < A$, if $f_{2n}/f_{1n} = A$ or B, a randomized decision is made between taking another observation and accepting the appropriate hypothesis. In the case $B = A$, if $f_{2n}/f_{1n} = A$, a randomized decision is made between the three possibilities of taking another observation, accepting f_1 and accepting f_2. In our example the ratio f_{2n}/f_{1n} takes on the values $1, -\infty$ and $+\infty$ (except that the ratio is not defined if $f_{1n} = f_{2n} = 0$), and the test of the preceding paragraph is essentially the SPR test with $A = B = 1$, except that randomized decisions are replaced by non-randomized ones.

It is of interest to note that the bound in (1.3) is always positive whereas the bounds in (1.1) and (1.2) take on the trivial value 0 if the integrals in their denominators are equal to $+ \infty$. However, in most of the common cases the bounds (1.1) and (1.2)(as well as (1.4)) are better than (1.3). For instance, if f_o, f_1 and f_2 are normal distributions with a common variance and respective means $0, -\delta$ and δ , the bound in (1.3) is of the order δ^{-1}, but those in (1.2) and (1.4) are proportional to δ^{-2} and hence better than (1.3) if δ is small.

3. Discussion of inequality (1.4). Strict equality in (1.4) cannot be achieved except in trivial cases. To obtain an idea of how close the bound in (1.4) can come to the mini-

mum attainable value of $E_0(N)$, we shall consider the following special case. Let f_i be the normal probability density with variance 1 and mean θ_i, where $\theta_0 = 0$, $\theta_1 = -\delta$ and $\theta_2 = \delta > 0$. Then $\zeta_1 = \zeta_2 = \delta^2/2$, $\tau = 2\delta$, and inequality (1.4) becomes

$$(3.1) \qquad E_0(N) \geq \delta^{-2} \{[1 - 2 \log(2\alpha)]^{1/2} - 1\}^2$$

where $2\alpha = \alpha_1 + \alpha_2$. This bound will be compared with the values of $E_0(N)$ for a fixed sample size test, Wald's SPR test, and a test considered by Anderson, with error probabilities $\alpha_1 = \alpha_2 = \alpha (< \frac{1}{2})$ in each case.

Let $S_n = X_1 + \cdots + X_n$. For a fixed sample size test such that decision d_1 or d_2 is made according as $S_n < 0$ or $S_n > 0$, the error probabilities at $\theta = -\delta$ and $\theta = \delta$ are both equal to $\Phi(-\delta n^{1/2})$, where

$$\Phi(x) = (2\pi)^{-1/2} \int_{-\infty}^{x} e^{-y^2/2} dy.$$

Hence $E_0(N)$ is the least n such that $\Phi(-\delta n^{1/2}) \leq \alpha$. If $\lambda = \lambda(\alpha)$ is defined by $\Phi(-\lambda) = \alpha$, we have

$$(3.2) \qquad E_0(N) = \delta^{-2} \lambda^2,$$

exactly or with a good approximation. If $\alpha \to 0$, then $\lambda \to \infty$ and[1]

$$\alpha = \Phi(-\lambda) = (2\pi)^{-1/2} \lambda^{-1} e^{-\lambda^2/2} (1 + O(\lambda^{-2}))$$

Hence

$$\lambda^2 = -2 \log \alpha + O[\log(-2 \log \alpha)].$$

The factor of δ^{-2} in inequality (3.1) is

$$\{[1 - 2 \log(2\alpha)]^{1/2} - 1\}^2 = -2 \log \alpha + O[(-2 \log \alpha)^{1/2}].$$

Thus if α is small enough, the bound in (3.1) is nearly attained with a fixed sample size test, although the asymptotic approach is extremely slow. It follows that the fixed sample size test nearly minimizes the expected sample size at $\theta = 0$ when α is (very) small.

Now consider the SPR test which stops as soon as $2\delta |S_n| > \log A (> 0)$. Then $(\log A)^2 \leq 4\delta^2 E_0(S_N^2) = 4\delta^2 E_0(N)$ by (1.8), and $A \leq \frac{1-\alpha}{\alpha}$. These inequalities are close approximations for α fixed and δ small enough (Wald [8]). With this approximation,

---

[1] Here $O(\lambda^{-2})$, order of λ^{-2}, denotes a term such that $\lambda^2 O(\lambda^{-2})$ is bounded as $\lambda \to \infty$. The O terms in the following equations have an analogous meaning.

$$(3.3) \qquad E_o(N) = \delta^{-2} \left(\frac{1}{2} \log \frac{1-\alpha}{\alpha} \right)^2 .$$

Put $\alpha = (1 - \epsilon)/2$, then

$$\left(\frac{1}{2} \log \frac{1-\alpha}{\alpha} \right)^2 = \epsilon^2 + \frac{2}{3} \epsilon^4 + \frac{23}{45} \epsilon^6 + \dots$$

and

$$\{ [1 - 2 \log (2\alpha)]^{1/2} - 1 \}^2 = \epsilon^2 + \frac{2}{3} \epsilon^4 - \frac{1}{6} \epsilon^5 + \dots$$

Thus if α is close to its upper bound $\frac{1}{2}$, and δ is small enough, the lower bound in (3.1) is nearly attained with a SPR test. Hence the SPR test nearly minimizes $E_o(N)$ in this case. Table 1 shows that even for $\alpha = 0.2$ the expected sample size exceeds the lower bound by only 3%. (The lower bound in (1.2) with $c = \frac{1}{2}$ also approaches $E_o(N)$ for the SPR test as $\alpha \to \frac{1}{2}$. However, inequality (3.1) is better than (1.2), as applied to the present case, for all values of α .)

For α values not close to 0 or $\frac{1}{2}$ we compare the bound in (3.1) with the expected sample size of a test considered by Anderson [1] . This test stops as soon as $|S_n| \geq c + dn$, where $d < 0 < c$. Anderson approximated the sequence $\{ S_n \}$ by a Wiener process so that his values for the expected stopping time, $E_o(\tau)$, when the mean of the process is 0 are approximations to $E_o(N)$. He chose the constants c and d so as to minimize $E_o(\tau)$ subject to prescribed error probabilities $\alpha_1 = \alpha_2 = \alpha$ at $\theta = \pm \delta$, for $\delta = 0.1$ and $\alpha = 0.01$ and 0.05. Anderson's values are given in Table 1. The expected sample sizes exceed the lower bounds by only 3.6% and 2.8% , respectively. This shows that both Anderson's test (as judged by the expected sample size at $\theta = 0$) and inequality (3.1) cannot be greatly improved in these cases.

Table 1

Values of $E_o(N)$ for $\delta = 0.1$ and $\alpha_1 = \alpha_2 = \alpha$

$\alpha =$	0.0001	0.001	0.01	0.05	0.1	0.2	0.3
Fixed sample size	1383	955	541.2	270.6	164.3	70.8	27.5
SPR test	2121	1193	527.9	216.7	120.7	48.0	17.9
Anderson's test	--	--	402.2	192.2	--	--	--
Lower bound (3.1)	1054	710	388.3	187.0	111.1	46.6	17.8

It is shown in [4] that for each of the two sequential tests here considered the expected sample size attains its maximum when the mean θ of the normal distribution is 0. In conjunction with the preceding results this implies that each of these tests (as well as the fixed sample size test) comes close to minimizing the maximum expected sample size for certain α values.

To summarize, we have seen that in certain cases the lower bounds for the expected sample size of a sequential test which are given by (1.3) and (1.4) come close to the smallest attainable expected sample size. We also have seen which tests come close to minimizing the expected sample size at certain parameter points. The bound in (1.3) can be strictly achieved for some special distributions which, however, are rare in applications. The bound in (1.4) is closely approached by Anderson's test for the usual values of α like 0.05 and 0.01 in the example which we have considered. (In Anderson's paper [1] it is shown that the expected sample size of his test when $\theta = -\delta$ or $\theta = \delta$ (in our notation) does not considerably exceed the smallest attainable expected sample size, that is, the test does only slightly worse than the SPR test at these parameter points.) Although in this section we have discussed only the special case of a normal distribution with mean θ, similar results undoubtedly can be obtained for many other common types of distributions when θ_0 is roughly midway between θ_1 and θ_2, and α_1 and α_2 are approximately equal.

BIBLIOGRAPHY

[1] T.W. Anderson, "A modification of sequential analysis to reduce the sample size," Ann. Math. Stat.

[2] T.G. Donnelly, "A family of sequential tests," Ph.D. dissertation, University of North Carolina, 1957.

[3] Wassily Hoeffding, "A lower bound for the average sample number of a sequential test," Ann. Math. Stat., Vol. 24 (1953), pp. 127-130.

[4] Wassily Hoeffding, "Lower bounds for the expected sample size and the average risk of a sequential procedure." Submitted for publication in Ann. Math. Stat.

[5] J. Kiefer and Lionel Weiss, "Some properties of generalized sequential probability ratio tests," Ann. Math. Stat., Vol. 28 (1957), pp. 57-74.

[6] J. Seitz and K. Winkelbauer, "Remark concerning a paper of Kolmogorov and Prohorov," Czechoslovak Math. J., Vol. 3 (78)(1953), pp. 89-91 (Russian with English summary.).

[7] Abraham Wald, "Differentiation under the expectation sign in the fundamental identity of sequential analysis," Ann. Math. Stat., Vol. 17(1946), pp. 493-497.

[8] Abraham Wald, Sequential Analysis, John Wiley & Sons, Inc., New York, 1947.

[9] Abraham Wald, Statistical Decision Functions, John Wiley & Sons, Inc., N.Y.1950.

[10] A. Wald and J. Wolfowitz, "Optimum character of the sequential probability ratio test," Ann. Math. Stat., Vol. 19 (1948), pp. 326-339.

[11] J. Wolfowitz, "The efficiency of sequential estimates and Wald's equation for sequential processes," Ann. Math. Stat., Vol. 18 (1947), pp. 215-230.

ON SOME ASPECTS OF MODELS OF COMPLEX BEHAVIORAL SYSTEMS[1]

David Rosenblatt

1. Introduction.

In this paper we propose to treat some formal and pragmatic aspects [13] of certain models of complex behavioral systems. These models relate to generalized resource flows and entail stochastic process representations of system activity.

For present purposes, the term 'model of complex behavioral system' is essentially intended to convey the following set of notions. First, we mean a formulation of the properties of an abstraction called an 'entity' relative to a discrete index set, the latter called <u>conventional system time</u>. Second, an 'entity' is in general taken to exhibit some distinguished <u>integral</u> properties which may be functionally stated in terms of the properties of its <u>proper parts</u>, but which no proper 'entity part' may manifest. Third, an 'entity' is regarded as a construction of certain distinguished proper parts called '<u>sub-entities</u>' in accordance with well-defined sets of rules of composition. In the systems of present interest, the parts called 'sub-entities' are taken to conditionally exhibit behavioral properties governed by specified finite-dimensional stochastic processes.

The particular models we propose to treat may be viewed as examples of complex behavioral systems drawn from two domains: the domain of <u>statistical economics</u> and the domain of <u>information logistics</u>. In effect, we consider certain provisional frameworks for the description of large-scale mass 'distributive' or 'flow' phenomena. These phenomena are construed as the conjoint outcome of the 'decision-making' activities of resource - connected 'entities' in time. The aspects which we take to be of special interest in this paper relate to the abstract concepts of <u>balance</u>, <u>closure</u>, and

[1] This paper was prepared as a part of the project "Symbolic Methods in the Study of Organizations" under Contract Nonr-1180(00) with the Office of Naval Research and with further support under Contract Nonr-761(05) of Project NR-047-001. Some of the results given here were presented in a preliminary version in a paper entitled "On Stochastic Process Representations of Economic and Accounting Activity, " read before Section K of the American Association for the Advancement of Science, December 30, 1958, in Washington, D. C.

interaction.

2. Relation Theoretic and Graph Theoretic Considerations.

The theory of finite homogeneous binary (or dyadic) relations developed by C.S. Peirce and E. Schröder [14, 20] may be taken to inform investigations of complex systems. A homogeneous binary or dyadic relation on a set σ of n elements $a_1, a_2, \ldots, a_n$ is construed as any rule ρ which specifies for each ordered couple (a_i, a_j) of elements of σ that either the relation ρ obtains between a_i and a_j (symbolically $a_i \, \rho \, a_j$) or that it does not obtain (symbolically $a_i \, \bar{\rho} \, a_j$) for i, j = 1, ..., n. It is well established that homogeneous binary relations defined on finite sets of elements can be represented in 1 - 1 fashion by means of two equivalent formalisms: (i) by finite Boolean relation matrices of zeros and ones [1, 14] ; and (ii) by finite directed graphs [11, 14] .

The 1 - 1 representation of binary relations ρ on σ by square Boolean relation matrices $R = \| r_{ij} \|$ (i, j = 1, ..., n) is defined by

$$r_{ij} = \begin{cases} 1 \text{ if } a_i \, \rho \, a_j \, , \\ \\ 0 \text{ if } a_i \, \bar{\rho} \, a_j \, . \end{cases}$$

The null relation $\overset{.}{\Lambda}$ then corresponds to the null matrix $\Lambda = \| r_{ij} \|$, $r_{ij} = 0$ for all i, j; the universal relation $\overset{.}{V}$ to the universal matrix $V = \| r_{ij} \|$, $r_{ij} = 1$ for all i, j [26] . The identity relation I corresponds to the identity matrix $I_n = \| r_{ij} \|$, $r_{ij} = 1$ if i = j and $r_{ij} = 0$ if i $\neq$ j for i, j = 1, ..., n. The relation-algebraic operations of negation, conversion, union, intersection, relative addition and relative multiplication may then be given relation matrix representation by means of the classical formalism of Boolean algebra. Thus, Boolean relation matrix multiplication corresponds to the operation of relative multiplication of relation algebra [1, 26] .

The graph theoretic representation of binary relations ρ on σ may be conveniently stated in terms of the 1 - 1 representation of finite-dimensional Boolean relation matrices by finite directed graphs. Given any square Boolean relation matrix $R = \| r_{ij} \|$, (i, j = 1, ..., n), the graph of R, G(R), consists of n objects $\alpha_1, \ldots, \alpha_n$ called vertices or points and the totality of ordered pairs of vertices $\overrightarrow{\alpha_i, \alpha_j}$ such that $\overrightarrow{\alpha_i, \alpha_j}$ exists if and only if $r_{ij} = 1$ in $R = \| r_{ij} \|$. The ordered pair (or edge or directed line) $\overrightarrow{\alpha_i, \alpha_j}$ is represented by an arrowed line directed from α_i to α_j, with arrowhead pointing toward α_j; edges of the form $\overrightarrow{\alpha_i, \alpha_i}$ are taken to be admissible for any vertex α_i

of G(R). A subgraph of graph G is a subset of the edges and vertices of G containing with each edge its terminal vertices or end points. With this 1 - 1 representation, it is then possible to designate the Boolean relation matrix R(G) corresponding to any given finite directed graph G. In this paper, we employ "graph" for "finite direct ed graph". Any given subgraph H of graph G, (H $\subset$ G), may then be represented by the submatrix R(H) (in the general sense of subrelation) of the Boolean relation matrix R(G) corresponding to G.

The Boolean matrix representation and, equivalently, the graph theoretic representation of finite nonnegative square matrices is of interest in the present study. Clearly any finite nonnegative square matrix may be regarded as a system of (nonnegative) 'valuations' imposed upon or assigned to a homogeneous binary relation defined on a finite set. Let $A = \| a_{ij} \|$ denote a nonnegative square matrix of order n. The square Boolean relation matrix $R_A = \| r_{ij} \|$ of order n is then defined by

$$ r_{ij} = \begin{cases} 1 \text{ if } a_{ij} > 0, \\[2mm] 0 \text{ if } a_{ij} = 0, \ (i, \ j = 1, \ldots, n). \end{cases} $$

For all finite matrix powers A^q of A and R_A^q of R_A the following holds: $r_{ij}^{(q)} = 1$ if and only if $a_{ij}^{(q)} > 0$, where $A^q = \| a_{ij}^{(q)} \|$, $R_A^{(q)} = \| r_{ij}^{(q)} \|$ for i, j = 1, ..., n. Here, $R_A^{(q)}$ is the q'th power of the relation matrix R_A obtained by conventional matrix multiplication subject to the usual Boolean rules for addition and multiplication of matrix elements: sum x + y = max (x, y) and product x · y = min (x, y), where x, y assume only values 0, 1 and the ordering 0 < 1 obtains [1] .

If A is a nonnegative square matrix of order n with Boolean matrix representation R_A, then the graph $G(R_A)$ will be called the graph of A. The sequence of powers $\{A^k; k = 1, 2, \ldots\}$ of A clearly entails the existence of a sequence of graphs $\left\{ G_{R_A k} \right\}$ which may, however, be shown to be finite in number as distinct graphs [17] .

We consider next a series of definitions relating to certain distinguished classes of graphs which depend upon the notion of connectedness. A vertex α of graph G is said to be connected to a vertex β in a subgraph H $\subset$ G if H contains edges

$$ \overrightarrow{\alpha, \gamma_1}, \quad \overrightarrow{\gamma_1, \gamma_2}, \quad \ldots, \quad \overrightarrow{\gamma_{m-1}, \gamma_m} $$

and $\gamma_m = \beta$. It is convenient, in this context, to say that in G β is attainable from α in m steps by means of a directed path.

We now introduce the concept of a "cyclic net". A subgraph $H \subset G$ is said to be a cyclic net of order m if and only if H contains m(m > 0) vertices of G and each vertex of H is connected to every vertex of H. A cyclic net H of order m in graph G is said to be simple or Peircean if and only if no proper subgraph $K \subset H$ is a cyclic net. A cyclic net H of order m in graph G is said to be maximal in G if and only if every cyclic net in G is a subgraph of H or contains no vertex in common with H. A cyclic net H of order m in graph G is said to be universal if for some positive integer q every vertex of H is attainable in q steps from some vertex α in H. A cyclic net H of order m in graph G is said to be closed in G if and only if H is a maximal cyclic net in G and every vertex of G attainable from any vertex in H is contained in H. The varieties of cyclic net may manifestly be depicted by diagrams.

It may be shown that a cyclic net of order $m \geq 2$ is universal if and only if the greatest common divisor of the orders of all simple cyclic nets contained therein is unity [17] . Clearly, a cyclic net is at once simple and universal if and only if it is of order one.

The graph theoretic concept of cyclic net may be shown to correspond biuniquely to the concept of indecomposability or irreducibility. A nonnegative square matrix A of order n is said to be indecomposable or irreducible if for no permutation matrix Γ (with transpose Γ^T) does

$$A_\Gamma = \Gamma A \Gamma^T = \left\| \begin{array}{cc} A_{11} & A_{12} \\ 0 & A_{22} \end{array} \right\| \quad ,$$

where A_{11}, A_{22} are square matrices [2, 7, 27] . The following theorem of correspondence may be established [17] : If A is a finite and nonnegative square matrix, then A is indecomposable (or irreducible) if and only if the graph $G(R_A)$ is a cyclic net. If the preceding Boolean representation of square matrices is generalized so that $r_{ij} = 0$ in R_A if and only if $a_{ij} = 0$ in an arbitrary matrix A, it is clear that the theorem of correspondence holds generally [9, 17] .

3. Concepts of Balance and Closure.

We consider next some formal properties of finite nonnegative square matrices which find significant applications in statistical economics, in the domain of generalized double-entry accounting, and in the theory of stochastic processes.

We first state two definitions relating to nonnegative square matrices of order n. A finite and nonnegative square matrix $A = \| a_{ij} \|$ will be said to be (row) substochas-tic if no row sum of A exceeds unity, i.e., $a_{ij} \geq 0$, $r_i \equiv \sum\limits_{j=1}^{n} a_{ij} \leq 1$ for all i; if each row sum of A is exactly unity the matrix is said to be stochastic. Next, a finite and nonnegative square matrix $X = \| x_{ij} \|$ will be said to be a balanced margin matrix (or to exhibit the balanced margin property) if each indexed row sum of X is exactly equal to the correspondingly indexed column sum of X, i.e., $r_i = c_i$ for $i = 1, \ldots, n$, where

$$r_i \equiv \sum_{j=1}^{n} x_{ij} \quad \text{and } c_i \equiv \sum_{h=1}^{n} x_{hi} \;.$$

To exclude the trivial case, we exclusively consider nonnegative matrices distinct from the null matrix. For the sake of historical definiteness, we will also call the balanced margin property for nonnegative (or, more generally, real) square arrays the Pacioli - Stevinus equalities [23] .

The preceding definitions can be given a concise formulation. Let g denote the column vector of dimension n with all elements unity. The nonnegative matrix A is stochastic if $Ag = g$ and is substochastic if $Ag \leq g$. The nonnegative matrix X exhibits the balanced margin property if $Xg = X^T g$.

Some of the formal relations which subsist between stochastic matrices and balanced margin matrices are of general interest and can be simply stated. To do this, we require two definitions. First, a linear system of the form $x(I - A) = w$, I the identity matrix, will be called a finite substochastic system if A is a substochastic matrix and w is a nonnegative (row) vector; if A is a stochastic matrix, the linear system is called stochastic. Second, a solution $\hat{x}$ of a substochastic system $x(I - A) = w$ will be called admissible if $\hat{x}$ is finite and nonnegative but not null. It is obvious that in a stochastic system $x(I - A) = w$, admissible solutions exist if and only if $w = \theta$, θ the null vector of appropriate dimension.

The following proposition which relates stochastic matrices to balanced margin matrices is of interest. Let D(u) denote a diagonal matrix containing the ordered components of a row (or column) vector u on the diagonal.

PROPOSITION 1: Let A be a stochastic matrix. Let $\hat{x}$ be a nonnegative row vector. Then $D(\hat{x})A$ is a balanced margin matrix if and only if $\hat{x}$ is an admissible solution of the stochastic system $x(I - A) = \theta$.

PROOF: Let e denote the row vector with all elements unity, viz., $e = g^T$. Directly, $eD(\hat{x})A = eA^T D(\hat{x})$ if and only if $\hat{x}A = \hat{x}$.

The preceding proposition simply states, in effect, that row normalization of a balanced margin matrix X with positive (row and column) margins produces a stochastic matrix A with the margin of X (written as a row vector) an admissible solution of the stochastic system $x(I - A) = \theta$; moreover, given an admissible solution $\hat{x}$ of the system $x(I - A) = \theta$, then $D(\hat{x})A$ exhibits the balanced margin property.

We observe but do not prove here, that if it is possible to obtain a stochastic matrix A by normalization of a given balanced margin matrix X, then all admissible solutions of the stochastic system $x(I - A) = \theta$ can be stated in terms of the (necessarily) positive margin vector eX and the graph $G(R_X)$ of X (cf. [19] and Theorem 3 of [18]). In fact, it may be shown that in the graph of an arbitrary (nontrivial) balanced margin matrix, to each index of a nonnull row there corresponds a vertex located in a closed cyclic net of the graph ([19] and Theorem 3 of [18]). Consequently, the graph of a (nontrivial) balanced margin matrix is composed of one or more disjoint closed cyclic nets and possibly contains isolated vertices corresponding to indices of null rows and columns.

We consider next a proposition relating to balanced margin matrices which finds application in certain general representations of "dynamic economic equilibrium" [6]. The proposition further applies to certain large-scale interindustrial ("input-output") models, multisector trade or exchange models, and formulations of macroeconomic stability (cf. [2] for bibliography). The fundamental abstract conception underlying all these models may be shown to go back directly to the stationary process representation of the Tableau Économique formulated by the biologist-philosopher François Quesnay (Tableau Économique, published in several versions in 1758 and 1759) [15, 21, 22] . The several studies of Quesnay constitute logical precursors of the investigations of A. J. Lotka and V. Volterra in mathematical biology [12, 25] ; the several studies, moreover, exhibit the strands of ancient philosophic doctrines. The original tableau économique representation employs a type of 'circular flow' or recurrent event formulation of generalized 'accounts' which are effectively stated in double-entry form [15]

The proposition of interest rests on the Perron-Frobenius theory of nonnegative matrices [7, 27] . This theory contains the following result: Any indecomposable (or irreducible) nonnegative square matrix A exhibits unique positive (normalized) left and right eigenvectors associated with a simple eigenvalue $\lambda > 0$ such that for any eigenvalue α of A, $|\alpha| \leq \lambda$. The eigenvalue λ of maximum modulus is called the spectral norm of A; in the following, all eigenvectors are conventionally taken to be nonnegative.

PROPOSITION 2: Let A be an indecomposable nonnegative square matrix with spectral norm ρ . Let x, y respectively be left and right normalized eigenvectors of A associated with ρ . Then D(x)AD(y) is a balanced margin matrix.

PROOF: Directly, $e[D(x)AD(y)] = xAD(y) = \rho xD(y) = \rho y^T D(x) = y^T A^T D(x)$
$= e[D(y)A^T D(x)]$.

From the standpoint of generality, it is clear that the generalized balanced margin property is intrinsic to 'eigenproblems': Let C be an $n \times n$ complex matrix with u, v left and right eigenvectors of C associated with eigenvalue λ . Then $S \equiv D(u)CD(v)$ is a generalized balanced margin matrix, i.e., $Sg = S^T g$.

The proposition we consider next contains some immediate consequences of the two earlier propositions (cf. [7, 27]).

PROPOSITION 3: Let A be an indecomposable nonnegative square matrix with spectral norm ρ. Let x, y respectively be left and right normalized eigenvectors of A associated with ρ . Let s denote the scalar (x, y) and let E denote the diagonal matrix $D(x)D^{-1}(y)$. The following then hold:

(i) $s^{-1}D(y)$ $[\frac{EAE^{-1}}{\rho}]$ $D(x)$ is a balanced margin matrix with margin given by

the stochastic row vector $s^{-1}xD(y)$;

(ii) $D^{-1}(x)$ $[\frac{EAE^{-1}}{\rho}]$ $D(x)$ is a (row) stochastic matrix with normalized left

invariant vector given by $s^{-1}xD(y)$;

(iii) $D(y)$ $[\frac{EAE^{-1}}{\rho}]$ $D^{-1}(y)$ is a (column) stochastic matrix with normalized

right invariant vector given by $s^{-1}D(x)y$;

(iv) $x[\frac{AE^{-1}}{\rho}] = y^T$ and $[\frac{AE^{-1}}{\rho}]x^T = y$;

68

(v) $[E\underline{A}] \; y = x^T$ and $y^T [E\underline{A}] = x.$
$\quad\quad\quad\rho \quad\quad\quad\quad\quad\quad\quad\quad \rho$

From the preceding proposition, it is clear that the 'extremal' y constitutes a <u>right</u> <u>unit</u> for the row stochastic matrix $D^{-1}(y) \; \underline{A} \; D(y)$ of (ii); analogously, the 'extremal' x constitutes a <u>left unit</u> for the column stochastic matrix $D(x) \; \underline{A} \; D^{-1}(x)$ of (iii).

The results of Proposition 3 find application in a formulation of the following charae-ter which occurs frequently in certain resource allocation problems (cf. [2] for refer-ences, and [6]). Consider an arbitrary but fixed nonnegative matrix A which may be taken to be a matrix of 'resource flows'. Consider next arbitrary positive vectors β and ω , such that β is an $(n \times 1)$ column vector and ω is a $(1 \times n)$ row vector. Let $\tilde{A}_{\beta,\omega} \equiv \tilde{A}$ denote the $(n+1 \times n+1)$ matrix

$$\left\| \begin{matrix} A & \beta \\ \omega & 0 \end{matrix} \right\| .$$

The matrix $\tilde{A}$ is clearly indecomposable or irreducible for in the graph of $\tilde{A}$ each ver-tex α_i $(i = 1, \ldots, n)$ is connected in one step to the vertex α_{n+1} which in turn is con-nected in one step to every vertex α_i ; there then exist at least n simple cyclic nets of order 2 in the graph of $\tilde{A}$. Moreover, if A is distinct from the null matrix, then the matrix $\tilde{A}$ is necessarily primitive (i.e., exhibits a single root of maximum modulus [7, 27]) so that all powers $\tilde{A}^k$ are surely positive for all $k \geq n^2 + 1$ [17, 27]. The matrix A is primitive if and only if the graph $G(R_A^\times)$ is a universal cyclic net [17]. But $G(R_A^\times)$ is a universal cyclic net if $a_{ii} > 0$ or if $a_{ij} > 0$ $(i \neq j)$; for the graph contains at least n simple cyclic nets of order 2 and $a_{ii} > 0$ or $a_{ij} > 0$ $(i \neq j)$ respectively entail the existence of a simple cyclic net of order 1 or of order 3 in the graph (cf. Section 2).

From the preceding propositions, it is clear that the indecomposable and nonnega-tive matrix $\tilde{A}_{\beta,\omega}$ can always be simply transformed so as to exhibit the balanced mar-gin property. Let $\tilde{x}$, $\tilde{y}$ respectively denote the normalized left and right eigenvectors of $\tilde{A}_{\beta,\omega}$ associated with the spectral norm λ of $\tilde{A}_{\beta,\omega}$. Clearly, $D(\tilde{x})\tilde{A}D(\tilde{y})$ is a ba-lanced margin matrix, where $\tilde{A} \equiv \tilde{A}_{\beta,\omega}$. Let $\tilde{x}$ be written as $[x, \; x_{n+1}]$ and $\tilde{y}$ as

$$\begin{bmatrix} y \\ y_{n+1} \end{bmatrix}$$

where x is a $(1 \times n)$ vector and y is an $(n \times 1)$ vector. Consider the matrix equations

(1) $$[x, x_{n+1}] \left\| \begin{matrix} A & \beta \\ \omega & 0 \end{matrix} \right\| = \lambda [x, x_{n+1}]$$

and

(2) $$\left\| \begin{matrix} A & \beta \\ \omega & 0 \end{matrix} \right\| \begin{bmatrix} y \\ y_{n+1} \end{bmatrix} = \lambda \begin{bmatrix} y \\ y_{n+1} \end{bmatrix}$$

By simple transformations and using the fact that $(\lambda I - A)^{-1}$ exists since $\tilde{A}$ is indecomposable, we then obtain

(3a) $\quad x = x_{n+1} \, \omega \, (\lambda I - A)^{-1}$,

(3b) $\quad y = (\lambda I - A)^{-1} y_{n+1} \beta$,

(3c) $\quad (\omega, y)/y_{n+1} = (x, \beta)/x_{n+1} = \lambda$;

equivalently, $\omega (\lambda I - A)^{-1} \beta = \lambda$.

By Proposition 3, the matrices $\mathcal{P} \equiv D^{-1}(\breve{y}) \frac{\tilde{A}}{\lambda} D(\breve{y})$ and $\mathcal{Q} \equiv D(\breve{x}) \frac{\tilde{A}}{\lambda} D^{-1}(\breve{x})$ are

respectively row stochastic and column stochastic. $\mathcal{P}$ has the left stationary stochastic vector $s^{-1}\breve{x}D(\breve{y})$ and $\mathcal{Q}$ has the right stationary stochastic vector $s^{-1}D(\breve{x})\breve{y}$, where the scalar $s = (\breve{x}, \breve{y})$. Thus, one may write $\mathcal{P}$ and $\mathcal{Q}$ in the following manner:

(4a) $$\mathcal{P} = \left\| \begin{matrix} D^{-1}(y) \frac{A}{\lambda} D(y) & D^{-1}(y) \frac{(\lambda I - A)y}{\lambda} \\ \frac{\omega D(y)}{\lambda y_{n+1}} & 0 \end{matrix} \right\|$$

(4b) $$\mathcal{Q} = \left\| \begin{matrix} D(x) \frac{A}{\lambda} D^{-1}(x) & \frac{D(x)\beta}{\lambda x_{n+1}} \\ \frac{x(\lambda I - A)}{\lambda} D^{-1}(x) & 0 \end{matrix} \right\|$$

Moreover, it is clear that one may express the relevant stationary (stochastic) vectors for $\mathcal{P}$ and $\mathcal{Q}$ respectively as follows:

(5) $\quad s^{-1}\breve{x}D(\breve{y}) = (p_{n+1} \, \omega * \{ D^{-1}(y) (I - \frac{A}{\lambda})^{-1} D(y) \}, p_{n+1})$,

where $p_{n+1} \equiv s^{-1}x_{n+1}y_{n+1}$ and the stochastic row vector $\omega * = \omega D(y) / \lambda y_{n+1}$;

(6) $\quad s^{-1}D(\breve{x})\breve{y} = (\{ D(x) (I - \frac{A}{\lambda})^{-1} D^{-1}(x) \} q_{n+1} \beta *, q_{n+1})$,

where $q_{n+1} \equiv s^{-1}x_{n+1}y_{n+1}$ and the stochastic column vector $\beta * = D(x)\beta / \lambda x_{n+1}$.

The matrix $D^{-1}(y) \frac{A}{\lambda} D(y)$ is row substochastic and contains no (row) stochastic principal submatrix; analogously, $D(x) \frac{A}{\lambda} D^{-1}(x)$ is column substochastic and contains no

(column) substochastic principal submatrix (cf. Theorem 1* of [18]). These proper-

ties follow directly from the essential indecomposability of $\widetilde{A}_{\beta, \omega}$.

It seems clear, from the development so far, that models of complex behavioral

systems (e.g., models of 'resource flows') involving interconnected or functionally

interdependent parts can under certain circumstances be formally depicted as Markov

processes, more specifically, as finite indecomposable Markov chains with discrete

parameter [3, 4, 5] . This is the case for certain representations which introduce

(finite) indecomposable nonnegative matrices and in which the concepts of 'balance'

(e.g., resource balance) or of 'stationary distribution' or of 'stationary flows' play an

intrinsic role [18] . In such cases, the transformed nonnegative matrix regarded as

the transition matrix of a discrete parameter (time homogeneous) Markov chain exhi-

bits a graph ('transition diagram') in which the vertices correspond to states and the

edges to one-step transitions between states. In many of these formulations, the pre-

ceding concepts are treated as equivalent to or are associated with some notion of

'equilibrium'. More generally, indecomposable structure is clearly not a requirement

for a Markov chain representation of such models [18] .

The notion of a balanced margin matrix is a relative concept. A proper principal

submatrix A of a nonnegative matrix C may in general exhibit the balanced margin pro-

perty when C does not; the converse also holds generally. Consider an indecomposable

nonnegative square matrix

$$C = \left\| \begin{matrix} A & E_{12} \\ E_{21} & B \end{matrix} \right\| ,$$

where A, B are both square and indecomposable. Let $z \equiv [z_1, z_2]$ and $w \equiv [w_1, w_2]$

respectively denote left and right eigenvectors associated with the spectral norm μ

of C; for convenience, let the individual component vectors of z and w be written as

stochastic vectors. Let x_A, y_A (x_B, y_B) respectively denote normalized left and right

eigenvectors associated with the spectral norm λ_A (λ_B) of A (B). In order that the

principal submatrices A, B exhibit the balanced margin property respectively for

$(x_A, y_A; \lambda_A)$ and for $(x_B, y_B; \lambda_B)$ when C exhibits the balanced margin property for

$(z, w; \mu)$ it is necessary and sufficient that the following hold:

71

(i) $\quad x_A E_{12} E_{21} = (\mu - \lambda_A)(\mu - \lambda_B) x_A,$

$\quad\quad E_{12} E_{21} y_A = (\mu - \lambda_A)(\mu - \lambda_B) y_A,$

(ii) $\quad x_B E_{21} E_{12} = (\mu - \lambda_A)(\mu - \lambda_B) x_B,$

$\quad\quad E_{21} E_{12} y_B = (\mu - \lambda_A)(\mu - \lambda_B) y_B,$

where the inequalities $\mu > \lambda_A$, $\mu > \lambda_B$ obtain and are consequences of the inde-composability of C [27].

We consider next the <u>closure representation</u> or <u>completion</u> of any finite substochastic system $x(I-A) = w$, $(I-A)$ singular or not. This representation enables a solution algorithm to be formally depicted as a finite-state time homogeneous Markov chain (discrete parameter); in effect, a 'computation' is replaced by an equivalent 'process'. In simple cases, the final statistical equilibrium vector coincides, except for a scale factor, with the solution(s) of the system $x(I-A) = w$. Closure bears a direct relation to balanced margin considerations.

The completion or closure representation of a substochastic system $x(I-A) = w$ of order n entails the embedding of the system in a well-defined stochastic system of order $(n+1)$. It then becomes possible to characterize the solution structure of the original system in terms of the solution structure of the containing stochastic system.

Consider a substochastic system $x(I-A) = w$ of order n, $(I-A)$ singular or not. The matrix $(I-A)$ is singular if and only if A contains a stochastic principal submatrix [18]; if $(I-A)$ is nonsingular, then the inverse may be stated in the form of the Neumann series, $(I-A)^{-1} = \sum_{h=0}^{\infty} A^h$. Let $\emptyset_w$ denote the sum of the components of w, i.e., $\emptyset_w = wg$, g the column vector with all elements unity. Let the row vector w* be defined as follows: $w* = \emptyset_w^{-1} w$ if $w \neq \theta_n$, $w* = \theta_n$ otherwise, θ_n the null vector of dimension n.

Let $\tilde{A}_w$ denote the square stochastic matrix of order $(n+1)$,

$$\left\| \begin{array}{cc} A & (I-A)g \\ w* & 1 - w*g \end{array} \right\| .$$

The stochastic system of order $(n+1)$, $\tilde{z}(I-\tilde{A}_w) = \theta_{n+1}$ will be called the <u>closure (representation)</u> or <u>completion</u> of the substochastic system $x(I-A) = w$ for given w, where $\tilde{z} = (z, z_{n+1})$, z a row vector of dimension n.

The following proposition characterizes the admissible solutions of a finite substochastic system in terms of the solutions of its closure.

THEOREM: Let $x(I-A) = w$ be a substochastic system of order n with closure $\check{z}(I-\tilde{A}_w) = \theta_{n+1}$. A vector $\hat{x}$ is an admissible solution of the system $x(I-A) = w$ if and only if $(\hat{x}, \emptyset_w)$ is an admissible solution of the closure of the system. The system $x(I-A) = w$ exhibits no admissible solution if and only if every admissible (left) stochastic solution of the closure contains a last component equal to $1 - w*g$.

PROOF: From the definition of closure, it follows directly that any substochastic system which exhibits at least one admissible solution is equivalent to the constrained stochastic system $(x, \emptyset_w)(I-\tilde{A}_w) = \theta_{n+1}$. It remains to consider the last statement of the Theorem. The 'if' part follows from the first statement since $1 - w*g$ can assume only the values, 1, 0. If $\emptyset_w = 0$, $1-w*g = 1$; and if $\emptyset_w \neq 0$, $1-w*g = 0$; both cases are inconsistent with the existence of admissible solutions for the system $x(I-A) = w$. We consider the 'only if' part of the last statement. There are two cases and these depend on the regularity of $(I-A)$. If $(I-A)^{-1}$ exists, admissible solutions fail to exist only if $w = \theta_n$. The index $(n+1)$ of $\tilde{A}_w$ is then an 'absorbing' index or state and, consequently, the unique stationary stochastic vector of $\tilde{A}_w$ is $(\theta_n, 1)$. If $(I-A)$ is singular, admissible solutions fail to exist only if the $(n+1)$'st row of $\tilde{A}_w$ contains positive entries in columns associated with one or more stochastic principal submatrices of $\tilde{A}_w$ (cf. Theorem 4 of [18]). The index or state $(n+1)$ of $\tilde{A}_w$ is then 'transient' and thus all stationary stochastic vectors of $\tilde{A}_w$ are null in the last component. This completes the proof.

The completion or closure $\check{z}(I-\tilde{A}_w) = \theta_{n+1}$ always has admissible solutions. This follows directly from the so-called mean ergodic theorem for finite stationary Markov chains (discrete parameter) [3, 4, 5] . The stochastic matrix

$$\tilde{A}_w* = \lim_{s \to \infty} s^{-1} \sum_{h=1}^{s} \tilde{A}_w^{h}$$

always exists and it is known that every admissible stochastic solution of $\check{z}(I-\tilde{A}_w) = \theta_{n+1}$ is given as a convex linear combination of the rows of $\tilde{A}_w*$ [3] . In the preceding result, relative to the non-existence of admissible solutions the 'testing scalar' $1 - w*g$ can assume only two values: 1 if $w = \theta_n$ and 0 if $w \neq \theta_n$. Admissible solutions fail to exist in the first case only when $(I-A)$ is nonsingular so that all the "probability mass" accumulates in the $(n+1)$'st state which is a unique absorbing state in the Markov chain with fixed transition matrix A_w. The second case of non-existence of admissible solutions occurs only when $(I-A)$ is singular and "probability mass" from the vector $w \neq \theta_n$ enters and irreversibly accumulates in the closed cyclic nets associated with one or more stochastic principal submatrices of A in the Markov chain with fixed transition matrix $\tilde{A}_w$ [17, 18] .

For finite substochastic systems $x(I-A) = w$ which frequently occur in some applications (e.g., in statistical economics or in generalized resource accounting [2, 10, 24]), viz. $(I-A)$ nonsingular, A nonnull, and w positive, the preceding Theorem leads to a simple iterative algorithm with possibly advantageous round-off and error-stability properties. The (infinite) algorithm may be made applicable under more general conditions but depending on the structure of the graph of the matrix A may have dubious efficiency, e.g., in case the matrix A is decomposable. Under the stated conditions, the stochastic matrix $\tilde{A}_w$ is the transition matrix of a regular Markov chain (with graph a universal cyclic net, cf. p.65) so that the powers of $\tilde{A}_w$ converge exponentially fast to a limit matrix equal to $\tilde{A}_w*$. The recursion $z_{k+1}(w) = z_k(w)\tilde{A}_w$ (k = 0, 1, 2,...), z_0 an arbitrary initial stochastic vector, accordingly converges exponentially fast to the limit "statistical equilibrium" distribution vector $\tilde{p}_w$ of the regular Markov chain, where $\tilde{p}_w = (p_{n+1}w*(I-A)^{-1}, p_{n+1})$. Clearly, $(\emptyset_w/p_{n+1})\tilde{p}_w = (\hat{x}, \emptyset_w)$, where $\hat{x} = w(I-A)^{-1}$. In short, the constrained solution of the closure is given by a scalar times the "statistical equilibrium" vector $\tilde{p}_w$, where the scalar is simply the product of the magnitude or measure $\emptyset_w$ in w by the mean recurrence time $1/(p_{n+1})$ of the closure index or state (n+1).

From these considerations, it therefore follows that if the substochastic system $x(I-A) = w$ (under the conditions, $(I-A)$ regular, A nonnull, w positive) is of large scale, then it may be solved without requiring the inversion of matrices of large order and without effecting scale-reduction or consolidation of the system $x(I-A) = w$ [19] . Consolidation of the system may, however, be of interest for essentially empirical reasons (as in some 'resource flow' models) rather than for formal or computational considerations. The Markov chain analogy (which is a successive approximations method) makes it possible to effect modifications in the matrix A (as well as in w) and also to utilize the (normalized) admissible solutions of earlier problems as initial vectors for the recursion in new problems. The matrix $\tilde{A}_w$ of the closure exhibits the balanced margin property in the form $D(\hat{x}, \emptyset_w) \tilde{A}_w$ and may be readily seen to be of the same form as the row stochastic matrix $\mathcal{P}$ considered earlier. The behavior of the powers of $\tilde{A}_w$ may be made evident by writing $\tilde{A}_w$ in the form:

$$\tilde{A}_w = \left\| \begin{array}{cc} A & \emptyset_n^T \\ w* & 1 \end{array} \right\| + \left\| \begin{array}{cc} 0 & (I-A)g \\ \emptyset_n & -1 \end{array} \right\|$$

From the Theorem, it is clear that certain 'balance' or 'equilibrium' problems can be stated in the formalism of finite-state time homogeneous Markov chains; indeed, many equilibrium conditions for models in statistical and mathematical economics follow as immediate consequences of the basic properties of balanced margin matrices. Conceptually, the stochastic process representation permits abstract formulations involving nonnegative square matrices to become as well models of "circulation" and "distribution" of abstract measure or "mass" [15] Such models may accordingly be taken to correspond to hypothetical random walks of elementary "mass" units (in some appropriate measure) on a directed graph or network in such manner that the potential statistical "observables", e.g., $(\hat{x}_w, \emptyset_w)$, are viewed as the expected outcomes of large-number replications of motion on the graph. The "circular flow" and "recurrent event" representations of this aspect of the powers of nonnegative square matrices is of an abstract character and quite independent of immediate economic or accounting interpretations. The representation, however, has established roots in the classical political economy (i.e., statistical economics) of the 18'th Century (in the Cantillon-Quesnay-Isnard tableau économique [21, 22]).

4. Aspects of Interaction.

We consider next some intrinsic aspects of interaction from the standpoint of the representation of complex systems. Consider first a system of recursions:

(1) $\qquad x_\alpha^{(k)} = x_\alpha^{(k-1)} A_{\alpha\alpha} + \sum_{\alpha \neq \beta} x_\beta^{(k-1)} A_{\beta\alpha} \qquad (\alpha, \beta = 1, \ldots, r; k = 1, 2, \ldots)$

where the matrices $A_{\gamma\delta}$ are nonnegative and of dimension $(n_\gamma \times n_\delta)$ and the initial vectors $x_\alpha^{(0)}$ ($\alpha = 1, \ldots, r$) are all nonnegative and nonnull; $\sum_{\alpha=1}^{r} n_\alpha = m$. The matrices $A_{\beta\alpha}$ ($\beta \neq \alpha$) will be called interaction terms $\{\beta, \alpha\}$ for the elements indexed α in the recursions; the matrices $A_{\alpha\alpha}$ will be called reflexive terms $\{\alpha, \alpha\}$ for the elements indexed α .

Given the convention on indices, the system of recursions may be written in the form

(2) $\underset{\sim}{x}^{(k)} = \underset{\sim}{x}^{(k-1)}B$ $(k=1,2,\ldots)$,

where $B = \| A_{\gamma\,\delta} \|$ (γ, $\delta = 1,\ldots,r$). Let B be an indecomposable and primitive matrix [7, 27] . Moreover, let B for convenience be a row stochastic matrix $P \equiv B$. The system of recursions can then be viewed as sub-computations in a larger computation or process in which the unique (left) stationary stochastic vector of P is to be determined as limit vector; the vectors $x_{\alpha}^{(k-1)}$ may be regarded as intermediate results which are transmitted between elements α in the course of an infinite algorithm.

Now let P be arbitrarily partitioned in a manner σ so that $P = \| C_{jk}^{(\sigma)} \|$ (j, k = 1,$\ldots$,p) where the matrices $C_{jk}^{(\sigma)}$ are of dimension $(n_j \times n_k)$. In analogous fashion, the matrices $C_{kh}^{(\sigma)}$ (k $\neq$ h) are called interaction terms and the matrices $C_{jj}^{(\sigma)}$ reflexive terms. Let P be written in the form $P = U^{(\sigma)} + R^{(\sigma)}$, where $U^{(\sigma)}$ is a block-diagonal matrix containing exclusively the reflexive terms $C_{jj}^{(\sigma)}$ and $R^{(\sigma)}$ contains all interaction terms.

Consider the nonnegative matrix $T^{(\sigma)}$ defined as $T^{(\sigma)} = R^{(\sigma)}(I - U^{(\sigma)})^{-1}$ which exists by virtue of the indecomposability of P, for we exclude the trivial cases of $U^{(\sigma)} = 0$ (the null matrix) and $U^{(\sigma)} = P$. The following relation then obtains:

(3) $P = U^{(\sigma)} + T^{(\sigma)} - T^{(\sigma)}U^{(\sigma)}$.

It then follows that

(4) $(I - P)(I - U^{(\sigma)})^{-1} = (I - T^{(\sigma)})$

holds. From the last relation (since P is indecomposable), it is evident that $T^{(\sigma)}$ is indecomposable with spectral norm unity. $T^{(\sigma)}$ and P then exhibit the same left stationary vectors; $T^{(\sigma)}$ is not necessarily primitive. If $T^{(\sigma)}$ is primitive, any system $\underset{\sim}{z}^{(k)} = \underset{\sim}{z}^{(k-1)}T^{(\sigma)}$ (where $\underset{\sim}{z}^{(0)}$ is nonnegative but not null) will yield the same (normalized) limit left stationary vector as the system $\underset{\sim}{x}^{(k)} = \underset{\sim}{x}^{(k-1)}P$. Depending on the partition σ and the structure of the graph of P, the limit vector may be determined by finite algorithm with great computational efficiency and without regard to primitivity.

Consider next a system of Boolean recursions (governed by the rules of Boolean algebra):

(5) $\Phi_{\alpha}^{(k)} = \Phi_{\alpha}^{(k-1)}R_{\alpha\alpha} + \underset{\alpha \neq \beta}{\Sigma}\, \Phi_{\beta}^{(k-1)}R_{\beta\alpha}$ (α, $\beta = 1,\ldots,r$; k = 1,2,$\ldots$),

where the relation matrices $R_{\gamma\,\delta}$ contain only elements 0 or 1 and are of dimension $(n_{\gamma} \times n_{\delta})$; $\underset{\alpha=1}{\overset{r}{\Sigma}}\, n_{\alpha} = m$. The Boolean relation matrices $R_{\beta\alpha}$ ($R_{\alpha\alpha}$) may similarly be called <u>interaction (reflexive)</u> terms for the elements indexed α in the recursions.

The system of recursions may analogously be written in the concise form

(6) $\widetilde{\Phi}^{(k)} = \widetilde{\Phi}^{(k-1)}R$ $(k = 1, 2, \ldots),$

where $R = \| R_{\gamma \delta} \|$ $(\gamma, \delta = 1, \ldots, r)$. The powers of Boolean relation matrices

have been characterized in [17] . The following result (Lemma 5, ibid.) is of general

applicability in computation and the representation of finite processes [18] : If in the

graph G(R) of a Boolean relation matrix R each vertex is connected to at least one ver-

tex, then there exists at least one closed cyclic net in the graph and every vertex of

G(R) is connected to one or more closed cyclic nets in G(R). If such a relation R were

in addition many-one, then the graph G(R) would be composed of one or more disjoint

subgraphs each terminating in a simple cyclic net ([17]and *96 in [26]). Each sub-

graph containing a simple cyclic net of order one is said to contain a <u>decisive</u> terminus.

5. Balance, Closure, and Interaction in Models of Complex Systems.

In this section, we exemplify the concepts of balance, closure, and interaction in

some simple formulations of complex behavioral systems.

a. Accounting Frameworks.

We consider first what is, in effect, the oldest flow network or matrix framework

for the description and control of subsystems; the framework was set forth in one of

the first mathematical works to be printed (in the West) by Fra Luca Pacioli in the

<u>Summa de arithmetica, geometria, proportioni, e proportionalità</u> (Venice, 1494). (In

the narrow sense of statistical economics, the following considerations apply to cor-

porate accounting, managerial and cost accounting, and accounting in the individual

domains of national income and product arrays, input-output flows, balance of pay-

ments, and money-flows accounting.)

Consider a classification grid or grating imposed on the 'transactions' of an orga-

nized 'entity' in which there exist m abstract collections; each collection is called an

'account'. The square grid with row and column indices j $(j = 1, \ldots, m)$ is called an

<u>articulation statement</u>. The row and column aspects for 'account' j are respectively

called '<u>debit j</u>' and '<u>credit j</u>' $(j = 1, \ldots, m)$. For some arbitrary 'time period' and in

some code of valuation or measure conventions, let $x_{ij} \geq 0$ denote the total 'measured

magnitude' of 'transactions' at once debited to 'account i' and credited to 'account j'.

It is conventional but not necessary that x_{ij} be taken to be nonnegative and that

$i \neq j$ $(i, j = 1, \ldots, m)$ in the preceding statement; in the following, then, x_{ij} may be real and i = j is admissible.

For the square matrix X of order m, let $\delta_i \equiv \max [r_i, c_i] - r_i$ and
$\gamma_i \equiv \max [r_i, c_i] - c_i$ where r_i, c_i are respectively the i'th row sum and i'th column sum (i = 1, ..., m). The square matrix $\widetilde{X}$ of order (m+1) is called the <u>effective closure</u> of the matrix X of order m if $\widetilde{X}$ satisfies the following bordering conditions relative to X:

$$\widetilde{X} = \left\| \begin{array}{cc} X & \delta \\ \gamma & 0 \end{array} \right\|$$

The effective closure $\widetilde{X}$ satisfies the Pacioli-Stevinus conditions identically and is a (generalized) balanced margin matrix. The row and column index (m+1) of $\widetilde{X}$ is associated with a collection called the '<u>balance-sheet account</u>' with analogous row-debit and column-credit names. The (m+1)'st row and column of $\widetilde{X}$ are in fact equivalent to the balance-sheet account. Moreover, $\sum_{i=1}^{m} \delta_i \equiv \sum_{i=1}^{m} \gamma_i$ is the fundamental debit-credit (or conservation) identity of all double-entry accounting.

It is noteworthy that in closed mathematical or statistical economic models which are 'arithmetized' in terms of articulated arrays of accounts, the 'equilibrium' and 'balance' concepts may become formally equivalent depending on the completeness of the 'closure'. In individual studies of resource flow systems, these concepts may have scientific or control utility where these possibilities may overlap.

b. "Input-Output" Representations.

We turn now to certain large-scale models of mathematical and statistical economics which are typically 'arithmetized' in accounting frameworks. These formulations include certain interindustrial ('input-output') models, multisector trade or exchange models, circulation models, and models of macroeconomic stability [2, 10, 18, 24] . Since all these formulations in a definite sense constitute simple examples of complex systems, we will for convenience refer to these as 'input-output' models; 'input' and 'output' may require redefinition from one model context to another.

The framework of certain of these 'input-output' models may be set forth in the following manner. At a given level of fine detail, a classification grid is imposed on the 'transactions' of an 'economy' in a generalized sense. The representation of the 'economy' is taken to be sufficiently detailed to possibly afford the specification of interac-

78

tion terms for multiplicities of 'subeconomies'. There are taken to be m collections

of 'entities' of analytic interest (e.g., establishments, firms, households, activities,

etc.). Each collection is called a sector, industry, activity, or component for 'enti-

ties' exhibiting a common property of analytic interest (e.g., producing or consuming

'similar' resources). A set of 'transaction' mass observables is assumed to be given

for some definite historical period or is statistically averaged over some well-defined

combination of time periods. The 'transaction' observables may be stated in terms of

the behavioral valuation conventions of the analytic 'entities' or they may be further

stated in terms of the consistent valuation conventions of the designer of the grid. Let

x_{ij} denote the valuation of purchases or procurements made by sector or activity i

from sector or activity j; let $x_{ij} \geq 0$ be called the value of input to sector or activity i

procured from sector or activity j. Let $\sum_{h=1}^{m} x_{hi} > 0$ be denoted by x_i and called

the value of output of activity or sector i. Let a_{ij} denote the normalized value of input

x_{ij}/x_i , and let it be called the unit input to sector or activity i from sector or activity

j: a_{ii} (i = 1,...,m) may but need not be null so that valuations may be uniformly ex-

pressed in 'gross' or in 'net' (i.e., $a_{ii} = 0$ for all i) terms. The sectors or activities

may have an implicit or explicit time reference and some activities may but need not

explicitly refer to 'investment'.

The 'transactions' matrix X is constructed to be in effective closure form so that X

is a balanced margin matrix, viz., $Xg = X^T g$. Let A* be the row-normalized form of

X where some or all of the matrix elements of A* are viewed as 'flow parameters'

(cf. Proposition 1). A* is a stochastic matrix and any proper principal submatrix A

of A* is obviously substochastic; some proper principal submatrices A may but need

not be stochastic.

Substochastic models of the form $x(I - A*) = \theta_m$, $x(I - A) = w$, for A any proper prin-

cipal submatrix of A* and w nonnegative, are respectively called closed and open input-

output models. In such models, interest centers on the admissible solutions of the sys-

tems which are regarded as 'activity level' vectors. In fact, such vectors are expres-

sed in valuation form relative to some base period reference point since any flow vec-

tor $\tilde{p}_w = (p_{n+1} w*(I - A)^{-1}, p_{n+1})$ of the completion of a nonsingular system $x(I - A) = w$

involves components of the product form $x_j y_j$ (j = 1,...,n+1), cf. Proposition 3 and

Theorem of Section 3. For models of this form, this fact was known to A. Isnard who in his Traité des richesses (Paris, 1781) essentially stated this result for a three-sector normalized resource model [21] . There also exist so-called "valuation" problems for such substochastic models which can be stated in analogous fashion and solved as stochastic systems in closure form. It is claimed that the "activity level" and "valuation" problems cannot be simultaneously solved in the substochastic models; this is the case, for the two problems as usually stated involve incompatible assumptions, viz., distinct 'income distributions' by activity or industry of origin. Both the "activity level" and "valuation" problems can be simultaneously solved in the simple closed model of production (or of 'dynamic economic equilibrium') in which it is required to 'balance' an indecomposable matrix

$$A_{\beta, \omega} = \begin{Vmatrix} A & \beta \\ \omega & 0 \end{Vmatrix}$$

with spectral norm ρ regarded as a 'growth' or 'reproduction' factor (cf. Proposition 3); the vectors $\tilde{x}$, $\tilde{y}$ of Proposition 3 are respectively called "activity level" and "valuation" vectors [6] . From the relations given in Proposition 3, it is clear that $\tilde{x}$, $\tilde{y}$ and ρ may be computed by means of well established successive approximations procedures. Immediately related to models of this type are closed 'period planning' models in which an indecomposable matrix $\tilde{A}$ contains only nontrivial nonnegative matrices $A_{\alpha \alpha}$ (reflexive terms) and $A_{\alpha, \alpha+1}$ (interaction terms) for $\alpha = 1, \ldots, r$ and also the interaction term A_{r1}; interest centers on the growth factor ρ and the left and right eigenvectors of $\tilde{A}$ associated with ρ .

From the preceding development, it is clear that these particular models and the issues which give rise to them can be equivalently formulated as balanced margin matrix problems or as constrained limit (possibly Cesàro limit) distribution problems for well-defined stationary Markov chains. In particular, consider an "activity level" problem for a nonsingular system $x(I - A) = w$, w positive and $A \neq 0$. The irreversible process (or computation) afforded by the Markov chain representation may clearly be regarded as a master phenomenological equation which entails individual sector "mass balance" at "equilibrium" and in which expected values are regarded as observables. In particular, the solution process is given by $\tilde{p}_{k+1} - \tilde{p}_k = \tilde{p}_k(\tilde{A}_w - I) \equiv \delta_k$, $\tilde{A}_w$ the closure of A (k = 0, 1, 2, ...). At "statistical equilibrium", $\delta_\infty = \theta_{n+1}$ and the limit vector $\tilde{p}_w = (p_{n+1}w*(I - A)^{-1}, p_{n+1})$ is independent of the initial vector. The scale

factor $\emptyset_w = wg$, and the aggregate gross "multiplier" for the system

$\mu_w \equiv (\sum_{j=1}^{n} \hat{x}_j + \emptyset_w)/\emptyset_w$ is simply given by the mean recurrence time $1/(p_{n+1})$ for

the index or state (n+1) of the closure, where $\hat{x} = w(I - A)^{-1}$. The scalar relation

$\hat{x}(I - A)g = wg = \emptyset_w = \hat{x}_{n+1}$ when written in the form $\sum_{j=1}^{n} (1-r_j)\hat{x}_j - \hat{x}_{n+1} = 0 (r_j \equiv \sum_{k=1}^{n} a_{jk})$

is designated as the "technical production-possibility function" for the 'economy' in

the input-output model since it is of invariant form for any 'bill of goods' or 'bill of

final demand' as w is called in these models.[1]

We continue this treatment of 'input-output' models by considering next a simple pro-

cess representation of certain accounting tableaus. We assume given a population,

elements of which are capable of effecting one-step transitions from 'state i' to 'state

j' (i, j = 1, ..., N) in a manner prescribed by a discrete parameter time-homogeneous

Markov chain with transition matrix $P = \| p_{ij} \|$ (i, j = 1, ..., N). To each one-step

transition from 'state i' to 'state j' (i.e., $\alpha_i \to \alpha_j$, α_i, α_j vertices in the graph $G(R_P)$)

there is assigned a 'valuation' c_{ij} as given in a real matrix $C = \| c_{ij} \|$ (i, j = 1, ..., N).

It is required to <u>additively</u> evaluate all possible k-step directed paths which have been

traversed by the end of the k'th period (k = 1, 2, ...).

Let $A^{[k]}$ denote the (N x N) 'path valuation' matrix at the end of the k'th period.

Since it is clear that $A^{[1]} = \| a_{ij}^{[1]} \| = \| c_{ij}p_{ij} \|$, $A^{[2]} = \| a_{ij}^{[2]} \| = \| \sum_{k=1}^{N} (c_{ik}+c_{kj})p_{ik}p_{kj} \|$,

$A^{[3]} = \| a_{ij}^{[3]} \| = \| \sum_{m=1}^{N} \sum_{k=1}^{N} (c_{ik} + c_{km} + c_{mj})p_{ik}p_{km}p_{mj} \|$, etc., the following

algorithm may be established for the path valuation' 'computation'.

ALGORITHM: $A^{[n]} = A^{[n-1]}P + P^{n-1}A^{[1]}$, n = 2, 3, ... This recursion, in effect,

decomposes the 'path valuation' into two distinct components and evidently requires no

valuation of individual paths. If the 'flow matrix' P were properly substochastic so

that $(I - P)^{-1}$ were to exist, the cumulative 'path valuation' would in the limit be simply

---

[1] A group-theoretic and stochastic process approach to a related set of resource models was given by the present writer in an unpublished paper entitled "On Some Struc-
tural Properties of Distributions of Income" (Harvard University, 1947-48), based on
researches in the period 1943-47, conducted at the Division of Statistical Standards,
U.S. Bureau of the Budget, and in other Federal research institutions, and cited in
Studies in Income and Wealth, Volume 13, National Bureau of Economic Research, New
York, 1951, pp. 385-386. Cf. also "The Distribution of Income and Consumer Behavior
Representations" (abstract), Econometrica, Volume 19 (1951), pp. 334-335.

given as

$$\lim_{s \to \infty} \sum_{n=1}^{s} A^{[n]} = (I - P)^{-1} A^{[1]} (I - P)^{-1} .$$

The preceding algorithm can be concisely stated in the following form. Let T denote the (2N x 2N) matrix

$$\begin{Vmatrix} P & 0 \\ A^{[1]} & P \end{Vmatrix}$$

The recursion or 'chain calculation' yields

$$T^n = T^{n-1} T = \begin{Vmatrix} P^n & 0 \\ A^{[n]} & P^n \end{Vmatrix} , \qquad n = 2, 3, \ldots .$$

The algorithm and recursion are obviously completely general in that they depend in no way on the properties of the matrices; thus $A^{[1]}$ and P could be Boolean relation matrices and the algebraic rules Boolean in character. In the latter case, the Boolean relation matrix $\sum_{h=0}^{\infty} P^h = \sum_{h=0}^{N-1} P^h \equiv P_*$ the 'ancestral relation' of the Boolean relation matrix P (cf. *91 of [26]); thus in Boolean terms $\sum_{h=1}^{\infty} A^{[h]} = P_* A^{[1]} P_*$.

We conclude this approach to 'input-output' formulations by considering a basic 'communication model' [16] . Let R be an (n x n) Boolean relation matrix and designated as the 'entity communication pattern' for entities placed in correspondence with the index set $1, \ldots, n$. Let S be a (p x p) Boolean relation matrix and designated as the 'message implication (or communication) relation' for messages (or ideas) placed in correspondence with the index set $\hat{1}, \ldots, \hat{p}$. Let T be a (non-homogeneous) (n x p) Boolean relation matrix and designated as the 'initial message input tableau' with row index set referring to the entities' and column index set referring to 'messages'.

Consider the 'communication model' defined by the Boolean recursive system

$$U^{[1]} = T, \qquad U^{[n]} = \check{R} \, U^{[n-1]} + U^{[n-1]} S \qquad (n = 2, 3, \ldots),$$

where $\check{R}$ is the converse (or transpose) of R. The recursive system specifies the "configuration state" of 'messages' held or known by the set of 'entities' in the course of system time. The recursion can be concisely stated in the following form. Let $\mathbb{O}$ denote the (n + p x n + p) Boolean matrix $\begin{Vmatrix} \check{R} & T \\ 0 & S \end{Vmatrix}$. The recursion or 'chain calculation' yields

$$\mathbb{O}^n = \mathbb{O}^{n-1} \, \mathbb{O} = \begin{Vmatrix} \check{R}^n & U^{[n]} \\ 0 & S^n \end{Vmatrix} , \qquad n = 2, 3, \ldots .$$

82

A classification of all 'communication' structures compatible with this model follows directly from the results given in [17] ; an algorithm for "minimum transmission times of 'messages' to 'entities' " can be readily stated [16] .

c. Information Logistics.

We consider finally a simple model of information logistics which belongs to the mathematical theory of censuses and large-scale sample surveys; it may also be regarded as a model of 'statistical audit'. In particular, we consider the outcome of information-processing operations as a topic in the theory of production where the 'output' chain is intrinsically treated as a sequence of classifications through a serial system of grids. Each processing operation is taken to be basically governed by a stochastic 'operator' (matrix). The 'output' of processing operation k is regarded as the 'input' to processing operation $k+1$. The expected 'reliability' or 'reproducibility' of the intermediate and final products is of interest in this model. 'Reliability' or 'reproducibility' is defined by certain balanced margin properties of expected joint distributions (or cross-tabulations) comparing the outcomes of first and second 'trial' of a given processing operation.

We designate the original collection of (census or survey) data as the initial processing operation and assume there exist a total of r operations $(j = 1, \ldots, r)$. The first operation may be regarded as the result of interaction between respondents and observers, where these may possibly coincide. Let the stochastic 'operator' for operation j $(j = 1, \ldots, r)$ be denoted by Ψ_j, where Ψ_h is a row stochastic matrix (generally rectangular), with column frame conformal with the row frame of Ψ_{h+1} $(h = 1, \ldots, r-1)$. Let Φ denote a row stochastic matrix which maps respondent 'cryptostates' $\beta_1, \ldots, \beta_L$ into response observables $\alpha_1, \ldots, \alpha_q$; the 'cryptostates' are generally unobservable and may not correspond in nature to response observables.

We assume given an initial distribution h over 'cryptostates' for some set of respondents. We further assume that there exists an $(L \times L)$ stochastic matrix Q governing transitions between 'cryptostates' for respondents in an interval between execution and repetition of the initial (census or survey) measurements. We prescribe <u>conditional</u> <u>independence</u> in all probability calculations. Since each of the processing operations is assumed to be repeated in sequence, we have in the first conjoint 'trial' the expectation

83

$h \; \Phi \; \prod\limits_{j=1}^{r} \; \Psi_j$ and in the second conjoint 'trial' the expectation $h \; Q \; \Phi \; \prod\limits_{j=1}^{r} \; \Psi_j.$

The expected joint distribution for first and second 'trials' is then given by

$$C(h) \equiv \left[\Phi \; \prod\limits_{j=1}^{r} \; \Psi_j \right]^T \; D(h) \; Q \; \left[\Phi \; \prod\limits_{j=1}^{r} \; \Psi_j \right] \quad , \quad \text{where } D(h) \text{ is a diagonal}$$

matrix. We define <u>reliability</u> or <u>reproducibility</u> of the information-processing sequence for h as the condition that the marginal distributions of C(h) be equal, i.e., $C(h)g = C(h)^T g$ so that C(h) must be a balanced margin matrix. In order that C(h) be a balanced margin matrix, given any arbitrary initial distribution h, it is necessary and sufficient that

$$\Phi \; \prod\limits_{j=1}^{r} \; \Psi_j \; = \; Q \; \Phi \; \prod\limits_{j=1}^{r} \; \Psi_j \; .$$

The basic consequence of the model then is that any expected joint distribution (or cross-tabulation) C(h) is necessarily symmetric.

6. Conclusion.

In this paper, we have considered the concepts of balance, closure, and interaction in the context of certain models of complex behavioral systems. In the study of complex systems, the remarks made by J.W. Gibbs in his address "On Multiple Algebra" (read before the American Association for the Advancement of Science, Section of Mathematics and Astronomy, 1886) [8] may be relevant: "In mathematics, a part often contains the whole".

BIBLIOGRAPHY

[1] Birkhoff, G.S., <u>Lattice Theory</u>, American Mathematical Society, New York, Revised Edition, 1948.

[2] Debreu, G., and I.N. Herstein, "Nonnegative Square Matrices," <u>Econometrica</u>, Vol. 21, 1953, pp. 597-607.

[3] Doob, J.L., <u>Stochastic Processes</u>, John Wiley and Sons, New York, 1953.

[4] Feller, W., <u>An Introduction to Probability and its Applications</u>, John Wiley & Sons, New York, 1950, Second Edition 1957.

[5] Fréchet, M., <u>Recherches théoriques modernes sur le calcul des probabilités, Vol. 2 (Theorie des événements en chaîne dans le cas d'un nombre fini d'états possibles)</u>, Gauthier-Villars, Paris, 1938, Second Edition 1952.

[6] Gale, D., "The Closed Linear Model of Production," in <u>Linear Inequalities and Related Systems</u> (H.W. Kuhn and A.W. Tucker, Ed.), Princeton University Press,

Princeton, 1956, pp. 285-303.

[7] Gantmacher, F.R., The Theory of Matrices, Volume Two, Chelsea Publishing Company, New York, 1959.

[8] Gibbs, J.W., Collected Works, Volume II, Yale University Press, New Haven, Reprinted 1948, 1957.

[9] Harary, F., "A Graph Theoretic Method for the Complete Reduction of a Matrix with a View towards Finding its Eigenvalues," Journal of Mathematics and Physics, Vol. 38, 1959, pp. 104-111.

[10] Hawkins, D., and H.A. Simon, "Note: Some Conditions of Macroeconomic Stability," Econometrica, Vol. 17, 1949, pp. 245-248.

[11] König, D., Theorie der endlichen und unendlichen Graphen, Akademische Verlagsgesellschaft M.B.H., Leipzig, 1936, Reprinted by Dover Publications, New York, 1950.

[12] Lotka, A.J., Elements of Physical Biology, Baltimore, 1925, Republished as Elements of Mathematical Biology, Dover Publications, New York, 1956.

[13] Nagel, E., Principles of the Theory of Probability, University of Chicago Press, Chicago, 1939.

[14] Peirce, C.S., Collected Papers, Volume III, Harvard University Press, Cambridge, 1933.

[15] Quesnay, F., Textes Annotés, François Quesnay et la Physiocratie, Vol. II, Institut National d 'Etudes Démographiques, Paris, 1958.

[16] Rosenblatt, D., "A Note on Communication in Organizations," Carnegie Institute of Technology (unpublished), 1951.

[17] Rosenblatt, D., "On the Graphs and Asymptotic Forms of Finite Boolean Relation Matrices and Stochastic Matrices," Naval Research Logistics Quarterly, Vol. 4, 1957, pp. 151-167.

[18] Rosenblatt, D., "On Linear Models and the Graphs of Minkowski-Leontief Matrices," Econometrica, Vol. 25, 1957, pp. 325-338.

[19] Rosenblatt, D., "On Aggregation and Consolidation in Linear Systems," to be published in Naval Research Logistics Quarterly, 1960;"On Aggregation and Consolidation in Finite Substochastic Systems I, II, III, IV," (Abstracts) Annals of Mathematical Statistics, Vol. 28, 1957, pp. 1060-1061; On Aggregation and Consolidation in Linear Systems, Technical Report C, Department of Statistics, American University, prepared under Contract Nonr-1180(00) (NR-047-012), August 1956 (ASTIA-AD-117-944).

[20] Schröder, E., Vorlesungen über die Algebra der Logik, 3 Vols., B.G. Teubner, Leipzig, 1890-1905.

[21] Schumpeter, J.A., History of Economic Analysis, Oxford University Press, New York, 1954.

[22] Schumpeter, J.A., Economic Doctrine and Method, Allen & Unwin, London, 1954.

[23] Smith, D.E., History of Mathematics, 2 Volumes, Ginn, Boston, 1923-1925, Reprinted by Dover Publications, New York, 1958.

[24] Solow, R., "On the Structure of Linear Models," Econometrica, Vol. 20, 1952, pp. 29-46.

[25] Volterra, V., Leçons sur la théorie mathématique de la lutte pour la vie, Paris, 1931.

[26] Whitehead, A.N., and B. Russell, Principia Mathematica, Vol. I, Cambridge University Press, Cambridge, 1910, Second Edition 1925.

[27] Wielandt, H., "Unzerlegbare, nicht negative Matrizen," Mathematische Zeitschrift, Vol. 52, 1950, pp. 642-648.

AN AGGREGATION PROBLEM FOR MARKOV CHAINS

M. Rosenblatt

Introduction. This is an expository paper which has as its aim a brief discussion of some problems in probability theory that have recently attracted some attention. Markov chains are among the simplest examples of dependent processes and have been used in models of random phenomena arising in a variety of fields in the physical sciences, social sciences and elsewhere. Often one may observe or deal with a function of the chain rather than the chain itself. This might be due to the fact that the raw data is too extensive and so is reduced by lumping or collapsing classes of states for greater ease in handling. It may also stem from the fact that the process of interest is not observed directly, rather only after it has been passed through some filter (possibly nonlinear). A natural question that arises is as to whether this function of the chain is Markovian itself. For if it were not (at least approximately) one might not be able to make use of the simple tools relevant when dealing with Markovian processes. In this paper some simple sufficient conditions are given under which the function of a Markov chain is itself a Markov chain. For simplicity, the problem is discussed in the context of a Markov chain rather than that of a general Markov process.

Definitions and Problems. Consider a Markov chain $X(n)$ (see [3]) $n = 0, 1, 2, \ldots$ with a finite number of states $1, 2, \ldots, m$, stationary transition probability (one-step) matrix

$$P = P^{(1)} = (p_{ij}; \ i, \ j = 1, \ldots, m)$$

$$p_{ij} = P \left[X(n+1) = j \, | \, X(n) = i \right] \geq 0$$

$$\sum_j p_{ij} = 1$$

and initial probability vector

$$w = (w_i)$$

$$w_i = P \left[X(0) = i \right] \geq 0$$

$$\sum w_i = 1.$$

The Markovian property amounts to

$$P[X(0) = i_o, \ldots, X(n) = i_n] = w_{i_o} p_{i_o, i_1} \cdots p_{i_{n-1}, i_n}$$

Note that this implies that the matrix of n-step transition probabilities

$$P^{(n)} = (p_{ij}^{(n)})$$

$$p_{ij}^{(n)} = P[X(n) = j | X(0) = i] ,$$

is given by

$$P^{(n)} = P^n.$$

We then automatically have the relation

$$P^{(n+s)} = P^{(n)} P^{(s)}$$

which is usually referred to as the Chapman-Kolmogorov equation. A natural problem that arises is as to when the Chapman-Kolmogorov equation implies the Markovian property. An example of Paul Lévy that will be given later on indicates that this is not generally true. Nonetheless we shall see that this does hold under some special circumstances.

Suppose the experimenter does not observe the process X(n) but rather a derived process Y(n) = f(X(n)) where f is a given function on $1, \ldots, m$. The states i of the original process on which f equals some fixed constant are collapsed into a single state of the new process Y(n). Call these collapsed sets of states S_i $i = 1, \ldots, r$, $r \leq m$. One would like to know whether the new process is Markovian. The following simple example indicates that this is generally not the case. Let the initial process be a Markov chain with three states $1, 2, 3$, transition probability matrix

$$P = \begin{pmatrix} 0 & 1/2 & 1/2 \\ 1/3 & 1/4 & 5/12 \\ 2/3 & 1/4 & 1/12 \end{pmatrix}$$

and initial probability vector

$$w = (1/3, \ 1/3, \ 1/3).$$

Collapse the states $1, 2$ into the set of states S. Then

$$P(X(n+2) \in S, \ X(n+1) \in S | X(n) \in S) = 29/96$$

$$\neq P(X(n+1) \in S | X(n) \in S)^2 = (13/24)^2$$

so that the new process is not Markovian.

<u>An Example of P. Lévy</u>. P. Lévy has given an example of a non-Markovian process whose transition probabilities satisfy the Chapman-Kolmogorov equation [4] . He has

called such processes pseudo-Markovian. The original process given by Lévy has a continuous state space but it is very easy to modify his construction and obtain a process with a discrete state space.

Consider a second order Markov process $Y(n)$ with m states, $m > 3$, and second order transition probability

$$P(Y(n+2) = u_2 \mid Y(n+1) = u_1, \ Y(n) = u_0)$$

$$= \frac{1}{m} \left\{ 1 - \cos \left[\frac{2\pi}{m} (2u_2 - u_1 - u_0) \right] \right\}$$

$$u_0, \ u_1, \ u_2 = 0, 1, \ldots, m-1.$$

Of course, the two-dimensional process

$$X(n) = (Y(n), \ Y(n-1))$$

is a Markov process (first order) in the sense specified in section one. But the process $Y(n)$, a function of $X(n)$, is not first order Markovian and yet its first order transition probabilities satisfy the Chapman-Kolmogorov equation if the initial probability distribution of $Y(n)$ is the uniform distribution $P(Y(n) = u) = 1/m$. The computations required to verify this parallel those given in Lévy's note [4].

Discussion of Problems. We shall discuss some of the results that have been obtained but shall not give proofs. Most of the proofs can be found in [2].

Often we are interested not in any initial probability distribution w but rather one, $p = (p_i)$, that is a left invariant vector of the matrix P

$$pP = p.$$

The process $X(n)$ is then stationary, that is, its probability structure is invariant under time displacement. Let D be the diagonal matrix with its ith diagonal entry p_i. The Markov chain $X(n)$ is said to be reversible if

$$DP = P'D$$

(P' is the transpose of P). This means that its probability structure going backwards in time is the same as that going forwards in time.

Theorem 1. Let $X(n)$ be a stationary reversible Markov chain with $p_i > 0$ for all i. Then $Y(n) = f(X(n))$ satisfies the Chapman-Kolmogorov equation if and only if

$$\sum_{j \in S_\beta} p_{ij} = P[X(n+1) \in S_\beta \mid X(n) = i] = C_{S_\alpha, S_\beta}$$

has the same value for all i in any given collapsed set of states S_α, $\alpha = 1, \ldots, r$.

In this case the condition that Y(n) satisfy the Chapman-Kolmogorov equation is equivalent to the condition that Y(n) be Markovian.

It would be interesting to obtain a neat set of necessary and sufficient conditions for a process Y(n) = f(X(n)), derived from a stationary Markov chain X(n) (not necessarily reversible), to be Markovian.

A somewhat different problem can be phrased in the following way. Let $w = (w_i)$, $w_i > 0$, $i = 1, \ldots, m$ be any initial probability distribution. Consider the Markov chain X(n) generated by initial distribution w and transition probability matrix P. Again consider Y(n) = f(X(n)) and require that Y(n) be Markovian whatever the initial distribution w.

Theorem 2. Given any set of states S_β generated by f, assume there are at least two states $i \in S_\alpha$, $i' \in S_{\alpha'}$, $\alpha \neq \alpha'$ such that

$$P_{i, S_\beta} = \sum_{j \in S_\beta} P_{ij} > 0$$

$$P_{i', S_\beta} > 0.$$

Then a necessary and sufficient condition that Y(n) be Markovian, whatever the initial distribution w of the Markov chain X(n), is noted below. Given any set of states S_β generated by f

$$\sum_{j \in S_\beta} P_{ij} P_{j, S_\gamma} = P_{i, S_\beta} C_{S_\beta, S_\gamma}$$

for all i and γ.

Examples satisfying the conditions of Theorem 2 but not those of Theorem 1 are given in [2], [7].

We shall now see that the Markov chains X(n) for which f(X(n)) is Markovian, whatever f may be, are of a degenerate form. Of course, a very strong condition is now imposed on X(n).

Theorem 3. Let X(n) be a stationary Markov chain with $p_i > 0$ $i = 1, \ldots, m$. f(X(n)) satisfies the Chapman-Kolmogorov equation for every many-one transformation f if and only if the transition probability matrix P of X(n) is of the form

$$P = \alpha I + (1 - \alpha)U$$

where U is a matrix with identical rows and α is a real number. Then f(X(n)) is Markovian for any f.

Let us now consider the case of a decent continuous time parameter Markov chain

90

with a finite number of states.

Theorem 4. Let $X(t)$ $0 \le t < \infty$ be a Markov chain with a finite number of states $i = 1, \ldots, m$ and stationary transition probability function

$$P(t) = (p_{ij}(t))$$

$$p_{ij}(t) = P[X(t + \tau) = j | X(\tau) = i], \ 0 \le t < \infty \ ,$$

continuous in t. Assume that

$$\lim_{t \downarrow 0} P(t) = I.$$

Clearly

$$P(t)P(s) = P(t + s) \ t, s > 0.$$

Let the initial probability distribution of $X(t)$ be $w, w_i > 0$, $i = 1, \ldots, m$. Then $Y(t) = f(X(t))$ satisfies the Chapman-Kolmogorov equations, whatever the initial distribution w of $X(t)$, if and only if for each $\beta = 1, \ldots, r$ separately either

(i) $p_{i, S_\beta}(t) \equiv 0$ for all $i \notin S_\beta$

or

(ii) $p_{i, S_\gamma}(t) = C_{S_\beta, S_\gamma}(t)$

for all $\gamma = 1, \ldots, r$ and every $i \in S_\beta$. Here again the condition that $Y(t)$ satisfy the Chapman-Kolmogorov equation is equivalent to the condition that $Y(t)$ be Markovian.

Bush and Mosteller [1] considered a problem similar to that of Theorem 3 and obtained the same result. B. Rankin [5] has discussed the condition of Theorem 1 as a sufficient condition for the collapsed $f(X(n))$ to be Markovian. One should also note that the conditions of Theorem 1 and Theorem 3 arise in aggregation problems as they occur in economics (see D. Rosenblatt [6]).

This research was supported by the Office of Naval Research. Reproduction in whole or in part is permitted for any purpose of the United States Government.

BIBLIOGRAPHY

[1] Bush and Mosteller, Stochastic Models for Learning, John Wiley & Sons, Inc.

[2] Burke, C.J. and Rosenblatt, M., "A Markovian Function of a Markov Chain," Ann. Math. Stat. 29 (1958) 1112-1122.

[3] Feller, W., An Introduction to Probability Theory and Its Applications, John Wiley & Sons, Inc.

[4] Lévy, P., "Example de Processus Pseudo-Markoviens," Compt. Rendus 228 (1949) 2004-2006.

[5] Rankin, B., "The Concept of Enchainment," an unpublished manuscript.

[6] Rosenblatt, D., "On Aggregation and Consolidation in Linear Systems," to be published in <u>Naval Research Logistics Quarterly</u>, 1960; "On Aggregation and Consolidation in Finite Substochastic Systems I, II, III, IV," (Abstracts) <u>Annals of Mathematical Statistics</u>, Vol. 28, 1957, pp. 1060-1061; On Aggregation and Consolidation in Linear Systems, Technical Report C, Department of Statistics, American University, prepared under Contract Nonr-1180 (00) (NR-047-012), August 1956 (ASTIA - AD-1171944).

[7] Rosenblatt, M., "Functions of a Markov Chain that are Markovian", Journ. Math. and Mech., 8(1959), 585-596.

CODING THEOREMS FOR A DISCRETE SOURCE WITH A FIDELITY CRITERION[1]

Claude E. Shannon

In this paper a study is made of the problem of coding a discrete source of information, given a <u>fidelity criterion</u> or a <u>measure of the distortion</u> of the final recovered message at the receiving point relative to the actual transmitted message. In a particular case there might be a certain tolerable level of distortion as determined by this measure. It is desired to so encode the information that the maximum possible signaling rate is obtained without exceeding the tolerable distortion level. This work is an expansion and detailed elaboration of ideas presented earlier[1], with particular reference to the discrete case.

We shall show that for a wide class of distortion measures and discrete sources of information there exists a function R(D) (depending on the particular distortion measure and source) which measures, in a sense, the equivalent rate R of the source (in bits per letter produced) when D is the allowed distortion level. Methods will be given for evaluating R(D) explicitly in certain simple cases and for evaluating R(D) by a limiting process in more complex cases. The basic results are roughly that it is impossible to signal at a rate faster than C/R(D) (source letters per second) over a memoryless channel of capacity C (bits per second) with a distortion measure less than or equal to D. On the other hand, by sufficiently long block codes it is possible to approach as closely as desired the rate C/R(D) with distortion level D.

Finally, some particular examples, using error probability of message letters and other simple distortion measures, are worked out in detail.

The Single-Letter Distortion Measure

Suppose that we have a discrete information source producing a sequence of letters or "word" $M = m_1, m_2, m_3, \ldots, m_t$, each chosen from a finite alphabet. These are to be transmitted over a channel and reproduced, at least approximately, at a receiving

---

[1] This work was supported in part by the U.S. Army (Signal Corps), the U.S. Air Force (Office of Scientific Research, Air Research and Development Command), and the U.S. Navy (Office of Naval Research).

point. (Here and throughout the paper, the words "reproduced" and "reproduction" do not imply an exact correct copy but allow the possibility of errors.) Let the reproduced word be $Z = z_1, z_2, \ldots, z_t$. The z_i letters may be from the same alphabet as the m_i letters or from an enlarged alphabet including, perhaps, special symbols for unknown or semi-unknown letters. In a noisy telegraph situation M and Z might be as follows:

$$M = I\ HAVE\ HEARD\ THE\ MERMAIDS\ SINGING\ldots$$

$$Z = I\ H\overset{?}{?}VT\ HEA?D\ TSE\ B?RMAID\overset{?}{Z}\ ??NGING\ldots$$

In this case, the z alphabet consists of the ordinary letters and space of the m alphabet, together with additional symbols "?", "$\overset{?}{A}$", "$\overset{?}{B}$", etc., indicating less certain identification. Even more generally, the z alphabet might be entirely different from the m alphabet.

Consider a situation in which there is a measure of the fidelity of transmission or the "distortion" between the original and final words. We shall assume first that this distortion measure is of a very simple and special type and later we shall generalize considerably on the basis of the special case.

A single-letter distortion measure is defined as follows. There is given a matrix d_{ij} with $d_{ij} \geq 0$. Here i ranges over the letters of the m alphabet of, say, a letters (assumed given a numerical ordering), while j ranges over the z alphabet of b letters. The quantity d_{ij} may be thought of as a "cost" if letter i is reproduced as letter j.

If the z alphabet includes the m alphabet, we will assume the distortion between an m letter and its correct reproduction to be zero and all incorrect reproductions to have positive distortion. It is convenient in this case to assume that the alphabets are arranged in the same indexing order so that $d_{ii} = 0$, $d_{ij} > 0$ $(i \neq j)$.

The distortion D, if word M is reproduced as word Z, is to be measured by the average of the individual letter distortions:

$$D(M, Z) = \frac{1}{t} \sum_{k=1}^{t} d_{m_k z_k}$$

If in a communication system, word M occurs with probability P(M) and the conditional probability, if M is transmitted, that word Z will be reproduced is $P(Z|M)$, then we assume that the over-all distortion of the system is given by

$$D = \sum_{M, Z} P(M)\ P(Z|M)\ D(M, Z)$$

94

Here we are supposing that all messages and reproduced words are of the same length t. In variable-length coding systems the analogous measure is merely the over-all probability that letter i is reproduced as j, multiplied by d_{ij} and summed on i and j. Note that D = 0 if and only if each word is correctly reproduced with probability 1 (in cases where the z alphabet includes the m alphabet), otherwise D > 0.

Some Simple Examples

A distortion measure may be represented by giving the matrix of its elements, all terms of which are non-negative. An alternative representation is in terms of a line diagram similar to those used for representing a memoryless noisy channel. The lines are now labeled, however, with the values d_{ij} rather than probabilities.

A simple example of a distortion measure, with identical m and z alphabets, is the error probability per letter. In this case, if the alphabets are ordered similarly, $d_{ij} = 1 - \delta_{ij}$, ($\delta_{ij} = 1$ if i = j; 0 if i ≠ j). If there were three letters in the m and z alphabets, the line diagram would be that shown in Fig. 1(a).

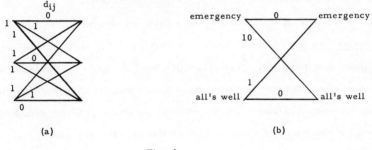

(a)   (b)

Fig. 1

Such a distortion measure might be appropriate in measuring the fidelity of a teletype or a remote typesetting system.

Another example is that of transmitting the quantized position of a wheel or shaft. Suppose that the circumference is divided into five equal arcs. It might be only half as costly to have an error of plus or minus one segment as larger errors. Thus the distortion measure might be

$$d_{ij} = \begin{cases} 0 & i = j \\ 1/2 & i - j = 1 \bmod 5 \\ 1 & i - j > 1 \bmod 5. \end{cases}$$

A third example might be an alarm system sending information each second, either "all's well" or "emergency," for some situation. Generally, it would be considerably

95

more important that the "emergency" signal be correctly received than that the "all's well" signal be correctly received. Thus if these were weighted 10 to 1, the diagram would be as shown in Fig. 1(b).

A fourth example with entirely distinct m and z alphabets is a case in which the m alphabet consists of three possible readings, -1, 0, and +1. Perhaps, for some reasons of economy, it is desired to work with a reproduced alphabet of two letters, $-\frac{1}{2}$ and $+\frac{1}{2}$. One might then have the matrix that is shown in Fig. 2.

Fig. 2.

The Rate-Distortion Function R(D)

Now suppose that successive letters of the message are statistically independent but chosen with the same probabilities, P_i being the probability of letter i from the alphabet. This type of source we call an <u>independent letter source</u>.

Given such a set of probabilities P_i and a distortion measure d_{ij}, we define a <u>rate-distortion function</u> as follows. Assign an arbitrary set of transition probabilities $q_i(j)$ for transitions from i to j. (Of course, $q_i(j) \geq 0$ and $\sum_j q_i(j) = 1$.) One could calculate for this assignment two things: first, the distortion measure $D(q_i(j)) = \sum_{ij} P_i q_i(j) d_{ij}$ if letter i were reproduced as j with conditional probability $q_i(j)$, and, second, the average mutual information between i and j if this were the case, namely

$$R(q_i(j)) = E\left[\log \frac{q_i(j)}{\sum_k P_k q_k(j)}\right]$$

$$= \sum_{i,j} P_i q_i(j) \log \frac{q_i(j)}{\sum_k P_k q_k(j)}$$

The rate-distortion function R(D*) is defined as the greatest lower bound of $R(q_i(j))$ when the $q_i(j)$ are varied subject to their probability limitations and subject to the average distortion D being less than or equal to D*.

Note that $R(q_i(j))$ is a continuous function of the $q_i(j)$ in the allowed region of variation of $q_i(j)$ which is closed. Consequently, <u>the greatest lower bound of R is actually</u>

96

attained as a minimum for each value of R that can occur at all. Further, from its definition it is clear that R(D) is a monotonically decreasing function of D.

The rate distortion function may be thought of as follows. Imagine various possible memoryless channels from the message alphabet to the recovered letter alphabet. A particular one of these corresponds to a choice of the $q_i(j)$ and may be called a test channel. For a particular test channel we calculate the average rate of transmission (average mutual information) and also the average distortion if this test channel were used without coding. The rate distortion function R(D) is the minimum rate for all possible test channels that have an average distortion not exceeding D.

Convexity of the R(D) Curve

Suppose that two points on the R(D) curve (that is, the curve R(D) plotted as a function of D) are (R, D) obtained with assignment $q_i(j)$ and (R', D') attained with assignment $q_i'(j)$. Consider a mixture of these assignments $\lambda q_i(j) + (1 - \lambda)q_i'(j)$ with $0 \leqslant \lambda \leqslant 1$. This produces a D'' (because of the linearity of D) equal to $\lambda D + (1 - \lambda)D'$. On the other hand, $R(q_i(j))$ is known to be a convex downward function (the rate or mutual information for a channel as a function of its transition probabilities). Hence $R'' \leqslant \lambda R + (1 - \lambda)R'$. The minimizing $q_i''(j)$ for D'' must give at least this low a value of R''. Hence the curve R as a function of D is convex downward. Conversely, because of its monotonicity, D as a function of R is convex downward.

The minimum possible D value clearly occurs if, for each i, $q_i(j)$ is assigned the value 1 for the j having the minimum d_{ij}. Thus, the lowest possible D is given by

$$D_{min} = \sum_i P_i \min_j d_{ij}$$

If the m alphabet is imaged in the z alphabet, then $D_{min} = 0$, and the corresponding R value is the ordinary entropy or rate for the source. In the more general situation, $R(D_{min})$ may be readily evaluated by evaluating R for the assignment mentioned, if there is a unique $\min_j d_{ij}$. Otherwise, the evaluation of $R(D_{min})$ is a bit more complex.

On the other hand, R = 0 is obtained if and only if $q_i(j) = Q_j$, a function of j only. This is because an average mutual information is positive unless the events are independent. For a given Q_j giving R = 0, the D is then $\sum_{ij} P_i Q_j d_{ij} = \sum_j Q_j \sum_i P_i d_{ij}$.

The minimum D for R = 0 clearly would result from finding a j that gives a minimum

$\sum_i P_i d_{ij}$ (say j*) and making $Q_{j*} = 1$. This can be done by assigning $q_i(j*) = 1$ (all other $q_i(j)$ are made 0).

Summarizing, then, R(D) is a convex downward function as shown in Fig. 3 running from $R(D_{min})$ at $D_{min} = \sum_i P_i \min_j d_{ij}$ to zero at $D_{max} = \min_j \sum_i P_i d_{ij}$. It is continuous (R a function of D or D a function of R) interior to this interval because of its

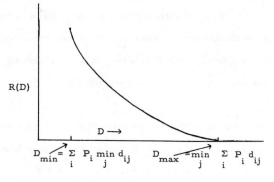

$$D_{min} = \sum_i P_i \min_j d_{ij} \qquad D_{max} = \min_j \sum_i P_i d_{ij}$$

Fig. 3

convexity. For $D \geqslant D_{max}$, we have $R = 0$. The curve is strictly monotonically decreasing from D_{min} to D_{max}. Also, it is easily seen that in this interval the assignment of $q_i(j)$ to obtain any point R(D*) must give a D satisfying the equality D = D* (not the inequality D < D*). (For D* > D_{max} the inequality will occur for the minimizing $q_i(j)$.) Thus the minimizing problem can be limited to a consideration of minima in the subspace where D = D*, except in the range D* > D_{max} (where R(D*) = 0).

The convex downward nature of R as a function of the assigned $q_i(j)$ is helpful in evaluating the R(D) in specific cases. It implies that any local minimum (in the subspace for a fixed D) is the absolute minimum in this subspace. For otherwise we could connect the local and absolute minima by a straight line and find a continuous series of points lower than the local minimum along this line. This would contradict its being a local minimum.

Furthermore, the functions $R(q_i(j))$ and $D(q_i(j))$ have continuous derivatives interior to the allowed $q_i(j)$ set. Hence ordinary calculus methods (e.g., Lagrangian multipliers) may be used to locate the minimum. In general, however, this still involves the solution of a set of simultaneous equations.

Solution for R(D) in Certain Simple Cases

One special type of situation leads to a simple explicit solution for the R(D) curve.

98

Suppose that all a input letters are equiprobable: $P_i = 1/a$. Suppose further that the d_{ij} matrix is square and is such that each row has the same set of entries and each column also has the same set of entries, although, in general, in different order.

An example of this type is the positioning of a wheel mentioned earlier if all positions are equally likely. Another example is the simple error probability distortion measure if all letters are equally likely.

In general, let the entries in any row or column be $d_1, d_2, d_3, \ldots, d_a$. Then we shall show that the minimizing R for a given D occurs when all lines with distortion assignment d_k are given the probability assignment

$$q_k = \frac{e^{-\rho\, d_k}}{\sum_i e^{-\rho\, d_i}}$$

Here ρ is a parameter ranging from 0 to ∞ which determines the value of D. With this minimizing assignment, D and R are given parametrically in terms of ρ :

$$D = \frac{\sum_i d_i\, e^{-\rho\, d_i}}{\sum_i e^{-\rho\, d_i}}$$

$$R = \log \frac{a}{\sum_i e^{-\rho\, d_i}} - \rho D$$

When $\rho = 0$ it may be seen that $D = \frac{1}{a} \sum_i d_i$ and $R = 0$. When $\rho \to \infty$, $D \to d_{min}$ and $R \to \log \frac{a}{k}$ where k is the number of d_i with value d_{min}.

This solution is proved as follows. Suppose that we have an assignment $q_i(j)$ giving a certain average distortion and mutual information, say D* and R*. Consider now a new assignment where each line with d_{ij} value d_1 is assigned the average of the assignments for these lines in the original assignment. Similarly, each line labeled d_2 is given the average of all the d_2 original assignments, and so on. Because of the linearity of D, this new assignment has the same D value, namely D*. The new R is the same as or smaller than R*. This is shown as follows. R may be written in terms of entropies as H(m) - H(m|z). H(m) is not changed, and H(m|z) can only be increased by this averaging. The latter fact can be seen by observing that because of the convexity of $-\sum_i x_i \log x_i$ we have

99

$$- \sum_j \alpha_j \sum_t x_j^{(t)} \log x_j^{(t)} \geq - \sum_t \left(\sum_j \alpha_j x_j^{(t)} \right) \log \sum_j \alpha_j x_j^{(t)}$$

where for a given t, $x_j^{(t)}$ is a set of probabilities, and α_j is a set of weighting factors. In particular

$$- \sum_j \frac{\sum_s q_j^{(s)}}{\sum_{s,i} q_i^{(s)}} \sum_t \frac{q_j^{(t)}}{\sum_s q_j^{(s)}} \log \frac{q_j^{(t)}}{\sum_s q_j^{(s)}} \geq - \sum_t \frac{\sum_j q_j^{(t)}}{\sum_{s,i} q_i^{(s)}} \log \frac{\sum_j q_j^{(t)}}{\sum_{s,i} q_i^{(s)}}$$

where $q_j^{(s)}$ is the original assignment to the line of value d_j from letter s. But this inequality can be interpreted on the left as $H(m|z)$ after the averaging process, while the right-hand side is $H(m|z)$ before the averaging. The desired result then follows.

Hence, for the minimizing assignment, all lines with the same d value will have equal probabilities. We denote these probabilities by q_i, each q_i corresponding to a line labeled d_i. The rate R and distortion D can now be written

$$D = \sum_i q_i d_i$$

$$R = \log a + \sum_i q_i \log q_i$$

since all received letters are now equiprobable, and $H(m) = \log a$, $H(m|z) = - \sum_i q_i \log q_i$.

We wish, by proper choice of the q_i, to minimize R for a given D and subject to $\sum_i q_i = 1$. Using Lagrangian multipliers,

$$U = \log a + \sum_i q_i \log q_i + \rho \sum_i q_i d_i + \mu \sum_i q_i$$

$$\frac{\partial U}{\partial q_i} = 1 + \log q_i + \rho d_i + \mu = 0$$

which yields the solution

$$q_i = A e^{-\rho d_i}$$

where A must be chosen to satisfy the side condition $\sum_i q_i = 1$. This requires

$$A = \frac{1}{\sum_i e^{-\rho d_i}}$$

We then have a stationary point and by the convexity properties mentioned above it must be the absolute minimum for the corresponding value of D. By substituting this probability assignment in the formulas for D and R we obtain the results stated above.

100

Rate for a Product Source with a Sum Distortion Measure

Suppose that we have two independent sources with respective distortion measures d_{ij} and $d_{i'j'}$ and resulting rate distortion functions $R_1(D_1)$ and $R_2(D_2)$. Suppose that each source produces one letter each second. Considering ordered pairs of letters as single letters the combined system may be called the product source. If the total distortion is to be measured by the sum of the individual distortions, $D = D_1 + D_2$, then there is a simple method of determining the function $R(D)$ for the product source. In fact, we shall show that each coordinate of $R(D)$ is obtained by adding the respective coordinates of the curves $R_1(D_1)$ and $R_2(D_2)$ at points on the two curves having the same slope. The set of points obtained in this manner is the curve $R(D)$. Furthermore, a probability assignment to obtain any point of $R(D)$ is the product of the assignments for the component points.

We shall first show that given any assignment $q_{i, i'}(j, j')$ for the product source, we can do at least as well in the minimizing process using an assignment of the form $q_i(j)q'_{i'}(j')$ where the q and q' are derived from the given $q_{i, i'}(j, j')$. Namely, let

$$q_i(j) = \sum_{i', j'} P'_{i'} \, q_{i, i'}(j, j')$$

$$q'_{i'}(j') = \sum_{i, j} P_i \, q_{i, i'}(j, j')$$

These are non-negative and, summed on j and j', respectively, give 1, so they are satisfactory transition probabilities. Also the assignment $q_i(j) \, q'_{i'}(j')$ gives the same total distortion as the assignment $q_{i, i'}(j, j')$. The former is

$$\sum_{i, i', j, j'} P_i P'_{i'} \, q_i(j) \, q'_{i'}(j') \, [\, d_{ij} + d'_{ij} \,]$$

$$= \sum_{i, j} P_i \, q_i(j) d_{ij} + \sum_{i', j'} P'_i \, q'_{i'}(j') d'_{i'j'}$$

$$= \sum_{\substack{i, i' \\ j, j'}} P_i P'_{i'} \, q_{i, i'}(j, j') \, [\, d_{ij} + d'_{i', j'} \,] \, ,$$

which is the distortion given by the assignment $q_{i, i'}(j, j')$.

On the other hand, the mutual information R is decreased or left constant if we use $q_i(j) \, q'_{i'}(j')$ instead of $q_{i, i'}(j, j')$. In fact, this average mutual information can be written in terms of entropies as follows (using asterisks for entropies with the assignment $q_i(j) \, q'_{i'}(j')$ and none for the assignment $q_{i, i'}(j, j')$). We have

101

$$R = H(i, i') - H(i, i'|j, j')$$

$$\geq H(i, i') - H(i|j, j') - H(i'|j, j')$$

$$\geq H(i, i') - H(i|j) - H(i'|j')$$

$$= H(i, i') - H*(i|j) - H*(i'|j').$$

Here we use the fact that with our definition of $q_i(j)$ and $q'_{i'}(j')$ we have $P*(i|j) = P(i|j)$ and $P*(i'|j') = P(i'|j')$. (This follows immediately on writing out these probabilities.) Now, using the fact that the sources are independent, $H(i, i') = H(i) + H(i') = H*(i) + H*(i')$. Hence our last reduction above is equal to $R*$. This is the desired conclusion.

It follows that any point on the R(D) curve for the product source is obtained by an independent or product assignment $q_i(j) \, q'_{i'}(j')$ and consequently (since with independent assignments both R and D are additive) is the sum in both coordinates of a pair of points on the two curves. The best choice for a given distortion D is clearly given by

$$R(D) = \min_t [\, R_1(t) + R_2(D - t)]$$

and this minimum will occur when

$$\frac{d}{dt} R_1(t) = \frac{d}{dt} R_2(D - t)$$

Thus the component points to be added are points where the component curves have the same slope. The convexity of these curves insures the uniqueness of this pair for any particular D.

The Lower Bound on Distortion for a Given Channel Capacity

The importance of the R(D) function is that it determines the channel capacity required to send at a certain rate and with a certain minimum distortion. Consider the following situation. We are given an independent letter source with probabilities P_i for the different possible letters. We are given a single-letter distortion measure d_{ij} which leads to the rate distortion function R(D). Finally, there is a memoryless discrete channel K of capacity C bits per channel, or for each usage of the channel. We wish to transmit words of length t, that is, containing t letters, from the source over the channel with a block code. The length of the code words in the channel is n, (that is, n channel letters). What is the lowest distortion D that might be obtained with a code and a decoding system of this sort?

Theorem 1. Under the assumptions given above it is not possible to have a code with distortion D smaller than the (minimum) D* satisfying

$$R(D*) = \frac{n}{t} C$$

or, equivalently, in any code, $D \geq R^{-1} (\frac{n}{t} C)$, where R^{-1} is the function inverse to R (take $R^{-1} (0)$ to be D_{max}).

This theorem, and a converse positive result to be given later, show that <u>R(D) may be thought of as the equivalent rate of the source for a given distortion D</u>. Theorem 1 asserts that for the distortion D and t letters of text, one must supply in the channel at least t R(D) total bits of capacity spread over the n uses of the channel in the code. The converse theorem will show that by taking n and t sufficiently large and with suitable codes it is possible to approach this limiting curve.

To prove Theorem 1, suppose that we have given a block code which encodes all message words of length t into channel words of length n and a decoding procedure for interpreting channel output words of length n into reproduced Z words of length t. Let a message word be represented by $M = m_1, m_2, \ldots, m_t$. A channel input word is $X = x_1, x_2, \ldots, x_n$. A channel output word is $Y = y_1, y_2, \ldots, y_n$ and a reproduced, or Z word is $Z = z_1, z_2, \ldots, z_t$. By the given code and decoding system, X is a function of M and Z is a function of Y. The m_i are chosen independently according to the letter probabilities, and the channel transition probabilities give a set of conditional probabilities $P(y|x)$ applying to each x_i, y_i pair. Finally, the source and channel are independent in the sense that $P(Y|M, X) = P(Y|X)$.

We first derive the known result that $H(M|Z) \geq H(M) - nC$. We have that $H(M|Z) \geq H(M|Y)$ (since Z is a function of Y) and also that $H(M|Y) \geq H(X|Y) - H(X) + H(M)$. This last is because, from the independence condition above, $H(Y|M, X) = H(Y|X)$, so $H(Y, M, X) - H(M, X) = H(X, Y) - H(X)$. But $H(M, X) = H(M)$, since X is a function of M, and for the same reason $H(M, X, Y) = H(M, Y)$. Hence, rearranging, we have

$$H(X, Y) = H(M, Y) + H(X) - H(M, X)$$

$$= H(M, Y) + H(X) - H(M)$$

$$H(X|Y) = H(M|Y) + H(X) - H(M)$$

Here we used $H(M, X) = H(M)$ and then subtracted $H(Y)$ from each side. Hence $H(M|Z) \geq H(X|Y) - H(X) + H(M)$.

Now we show that $H(X|Y) \geq H(X) - nC$. This follows from a method we have used in other similar situations, by considering the <u>change</u> in $H(X|Y)$ with each received let-

103

ter. Thus (using Y_k for the first k y-letters, etc.),

$$\Delta H(X|Y) = H(X|y_1, y_2, \ldots, y_k) - H(X|y_1, y_2, \ldots, y_{k+1})$$

$$= H(X, Y_k) - H(Y_k) - H(X, Y_k, y_{k+1}) + H(Y_k, y_{k+1})$$

$$= H(y_{k+1}|Y_k) - H(y_{k+1}|X, Y_k)$$

$$= H(y_{k+1}|Y_k) - H(y_{k+1}|x_{k+1})$$

$$\leq H(y_{k+1}) - H(y_{k+1}|x_{k+1})$$

$$\leq C$$

Here we used to obtain the fourth line, the fact that the channel is memoryless, so $P(y_{k+1}|X, Y_k) = P(y_{k+1}|x_{k+1})$ and therefore $H(y_{k+1}|X, Y_k) = H(y_{k+1}|x_{k+1})$. Finally, C is the maximum possible $H(y) - H(y|x)$ giving the last inequality.

Since the incremental change in $H(X|Y_k)$ is bounded by C, the total change after n steps is bounded by nC. Consequently, the final $H(X|Y)$ is at least the initial value $H(X)$ less nC.

$$H(M|Z) \geq H(X|Y) - H(X) + H(M)$$

$$\geq H(X) - nC - H(X) + H(M)$$

$$H(M|Z) \geq H(M) - nC$$

We now wish to <u>overbound</u> $H(M|Z)$ in terms of the distortion D. We have

$$H(M|Z) = H(m_1 m_2 \cdots m_t | z_1 z_2 \cdots z_t)$$

$$\leq \sum_i H(m_1, m_2, \ldots, m_t | z_i)$$

$$\leq \sum_i H(m_i|z_i)$$

$$= \sum_i H(m_i) - \sum_i (H(m_i) - H(m_i|z_i))$$

Here we used the fact that additional conditioning variables decrease entropy and also the entropy of a joint event is as large as that of any one of the events. The quantity $H(m_i) - H(m_i|z_i)$ is the average mutual information between original message letter m_i and reproduced letter z_i. If we let D_i be the distortion between these letters, then $R(D_i)$ (the rate-distortion function evaluated for this D_i) satisfies

$$R(D_i) \leq H(m_i) - H(m_i|z_i)$$

since $R(D_i)$ is the minimum mutual information for the distortion D_i with any probability assignment. Hence our inequality may be written

104

$$H(M \mid Z) \leq \sum_{i=1}^{t} H(m_i) - \sum_{i=1}^{t} R(D_i)$$

Using now the fact that R(D) is a convex downward function, we have

$$H(M \mid Z) \leq \sum_{i} H(m_i) - t R\left(\sum_{i} \frac{D_i}{t} \right)$$

But $\sum_{i} \dfrac{D_i}{t} = D$, the over-all distortion of the system, so

$$H(M \mid Z) \leq \sum_{i} H(m_i) - t R(D)$$

Combining this with our previous lower bound and using the independent letter assumption, so $H(M) = \sum_{i} H(m_i)$, we have

$$H(M) - nC \leq H(M) - t R(D)$$

$$nC \leq t R(D)$$

Since R(D) is monotone decreasing, this requires that $D \geq D^*$, the value resulting in equality $nC = t R(D^*)$. This is essentially the result stated in Theorem 1.

It should be noted that the result in the theorem is an assertion about the minimum distortion after any finite number n of uses of the channel. It is not an asymptotic result for large n. Also, it applies, as seen by the method of proof, for any code, block or variable length, provided only that after n uses of the channel, t (or more) letters are produced at the receiving point, whatever the received sequence may be.

The Coding Theorem for a Single-Letter Distortion Measure

We now prove a positive coding theorem corresponding to the negative statements of Theorem 1; namely, that it is possible to approach the lower bound of distortion for a given ratio of number n of channel letters to number t of message letters. We consider then a source of message letters and a single-letter distortion measure d_{ij}. More generally than Theorem 1, however, this source may be any ergodic source; it is not necessarily an independent letter source. This more general situation will be helpful in a later generalization of the theorem. For an ergodic source there will still, of course, be letter probabilities P_i, and we could determine a rate distortion function R(D) based on these probabilities as though it were an independent letter source.

We first establish the following result.

Lemma 1. Suppose that we have an ergodic source with letter probabilities P_i, a

105

single-letter distortion measure d_{ij}, and a set of assigned transition probabilities $q_i(j)$ such that

$$\sum_{i,j} P_i \, q_i(j) \, d_{ij} = D*$$

$$\sum_{i,j} P_i \, q_i(j) \log \frac{q_i(j)}{\sum_{k} P_k \, q_k(j)} = R$$

Let Q(Z) be the probability measure of a sequence Z in the space of reproduced sequences of length t if successive source letters had independent transition probabilities $q_i(j)$ into the Z alphabet. Then, given any $\epsilon > 0$, for all sufficiently large block length t, there exists a set α of messages of length t from the source with total source probability $P(\alpha) \geqslant 1 - \epsilon$, and for each M belonging to α a set of Z sequences of length t, say β_M, such that

1) $D(M, Z) \leqslant D* + \epsilon$ for $M \in \alpha$ and $Z \in \beta_M$

2) $Q(\beta_M) \geqslant e^{-t(R+\epsilon)}$ for any $M \in \alpha$

In other words, and somewhat roughly, long messages will, with high probability, fall in a certain subset α. Each member M of this subset has an associated set of Z sequences β_M. The members of β_M have only (at most) slightly more than D* distortion with M and the logarithm of the total probability of β_M in the Q measure is almost -t R.

To prove the lemma, consider source blocks of length t and the Z blocks of length t. Consider the two random variables, the distortion D between an M block and a Z block and the (unaveraged) mutual information I(M, Z) given by:

$$D = \frac{1}{t} \sum_i d_{m_i z_i}$$

$$I(M, Z) = \frac{1}{t} \log \frac{Pr(Z|M)}{Q(Z)} = \frac{1}{t} \sum_i \log \frac{Pr(z_i|m_i)}{Q(z_i)}$$

Here m_i is the ith letter of a source block M, and z_i is the ith letter of a Z block. Both I and D are random variables, taking on different values corresponding to different choices of M and Z. They are both the sum of t random variables which are identical functions of the joint M Z process except for shifting along over t positions.

Since the joint process is ergodic, we may apply the ergodic theorem and assert that when t is large, D and I will, with probability nearly 1, be close to their expected

106

values. In particular, for any given ϵ_1 and δ, if t is sufficiently large, we will have with probability $\geq 1 - \dfrac{\delta^2}{2}$ that $D \leq \displaystyle\sum_{i,j} P_i\, q_i(j)\, d_{ij} + \epsilon_1 = D* + \epsilon_1$. Also, with probability at least $1 - \dfrac{\delta^2}{2}$ we will have

$$I \leq \sum_{i,j} P_i\, q_i(j) \log \frac{q_i(j)}{Q_j} + \epsilon_1 = R(D*) + \epsilon_1$$

Let γ be the set of (M, Z) pairs for which <u>both</u> inequalities hold. Then $P(\gamma) \geq 1 - \delta^2$ because each of the conditions can exclude, at most, a set of probability $\delta^2/2$. Now for any M_1 define β_{M_1} as the set of Z such that (M_1, Z) belongs to γ.

We have

$$P(\beta_M | M) \geq 1 - \delta$$

on a set α of M whose total probability satisfies $P(\alpha) \geq 1 - \delta$. This is true, since if it were not we would have a total probability in the set complementary to γ of at least $\delta \cdot \delta = \delta^2$, a contradiction. The first δ would be the probability of M not being in α, and the second δ the conditional probability for such M's of Z not being in β_M. The product gives a lower bound on the probability of the complementary set to γ.

If $z \in \beta_{M_1}$, then

$$\frac{1}{t} \log \frac{P(Z|M_1)}{Q(Z)} \leq R(D*) + \epsilon_1$$

$$Q(Z) \geq P(Z|M_1) e^{-t(R(D*) + \epsilon_1)}$$

Sum this inequality over all $Z \in \beta_{M_1}$.

$$Q(\beta_M) = \sum_{Z \in \beta_{M_1}} Q(Z) \geq e^{-t(R + \epsilon_1)} \sum_{Z \in \beta_{M_1}} P(Z|M_1)$$

If $M_1 \in \alpha$ then $\displaystyle\sum_{Z \in \beta_{M_1}} P(Z|M_1) \geq 1 - \delta$ as seen above. Hence the inequality can be continued to give

$$Q(\beta_{M_1}) \geq (1 - \delta)\, e^{-t(R + \epsilon_1)} \qquad M_1 \in \alpha$$

We have now established that for any $\epsilon_1 > 0$ and $\delta > 0$ there exists (for sufficiently large block length t) a set α of M's and sets β_M of Z's defined for each M in α with the three properties

    1) $\Pr(\alpha) \geq 1 - \delta$

2) $D(Z, M) \leqslant D^* + \epsilon_1$ if $M \in \alpha$, $Z \in \beta_M$

3) $Q(\beta_M) \geqslant (1 - \delta) e^{-t(R + \epsilon_1)}$ if $M \in \alpha$

provided that the block length t is sufficiently large. Clearly, this implies that for any

$\epsilon > 0$ and sufficiently large t we will have

1) $Pr(\alpha) \geqslant 1 - \epsilon$

2) $D(Z, M) \leqslant D^* + \epsilon$ if $M \in \alpha$, $Z \in \beta_M$

3) $Q(\beta_M) \geqslant e^{-t(R + \epsilon)}$ if $M \in \alpha$

since we may take the ϵ_1 and δ sufficiently small to satisfy these simplified conditions

in which we use the same ϵ. This concludes the proof of the lemma.

Before attacking the general coding problem, we consider the problem indicated

schematically in Fig. 4.

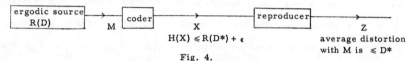

$H(X) \leqslant R(D^*) + \epsilon$ — average distortion with M is $\leqslant D^*$

Fig. 4.

We have an ergodic source and a single-letter distortion measure that gives the rate

distortion function based on single letter probabilities R(D). It is desired to encode

this source by a coder into sequences X in such a way that the original messages can be

reproduced by the reproducer with an average distortion that does not exceed D* (D* be-

ing some fixed tolerable distortion level). We are considering here block coding de-

vices for both boxes. Thus the coder takes as input successive blocks of length t pro-

duced by the source and has, as output, corresponding to each possible M block, a

block from an X alphabet.

The aim here is to do the coding in such a way as to keep the entropy of the X sequen-

ces as low as possible, subject to this requirement of reproducibility with distortion D*

or less. Here the entropy to which we are referring is the entropy per letter of the ori-

ginal source. (Alternatively, we might think of the source as producing one letter per

second and we are then interested in the X entropy per second.)

We shall show that for any D* and any $\epsilon > 0$ coders and reproducers can be found that

are such that $H(X) \leqslant R(D^*) + \epsilon$. As $\epsilon \to 0$ the block length involved in the code in general

increases. This result, of course, is closely related to our interpretation of R(D*) as

the equivalent rate of the source for distortion D*. It will follow readily from the following theorem.

Theorem 2. Given an ergodic source, a distortion measure d_{ij}, and rate distortion function R(D) (based on the single-letter frequencies of the source), given $D* \geqslant D_{min}$ and $\delta > 0$, then for any sufficiently large t there exists a set Λ containing N words of length t in the z alphabet with the following properties:

1) $\frac{1}{t} \log N \leqslant R(D*) + \delta$

2) The average distortion between an M word of length t and its nearest

(i.e., least distortion) word in the set Λ is less than or equal to $D* + \delta$.

This theorem implies (except for the δ in property (2) which will later be eliminated) the results mentioned above. Namely, for the coder, one merely uses a device that maps any M word into its nearest member of Λ . The reproducer is then merely an identity transformation. The entropy per source letter of the coded sequence cannot exceed $R(D*) + \delta$, since this would be maximized at $\frac{1}{t} \log N$ if all of the N members of Λ were equally probable and $\frac{1}{t} \log N$ is by the theorem to be less than or equal to $R(D*) + \delta$.

This theorem will be proved by a random coding argument. We shall consider an ensemble of ways of selecting the members of Λ and estimate the average distortion for this ensemble. From the bounds on the average it will follow that at least one code exists in the ensemble with the desired properties.

The ensemble of codes is defined as follows. For the given D* there will be a set of transition probabilities $q_i(j)$ that result in the minimum R, that is, R(D*). The set of letter probabilities, together with these transition probabilities, induce a measure Q(Z) in the space of reproduced words. The Q measure for a single z letter, say letter j, is $\sum_i P_i q_i(j)$. The Q measure for a Z word consisting of letters $j_1, j_2, \ldots, j_t$ is

$$Q(Z) = \prod_{k=1}^{t} \left(\sum_i P_i q_i(j_k) \right).$$

In the ensemble of codes of length t, the integers from 1 to N are mapped into Z words of length t in all possible ways. An integer is mapped into a particular word Z_1, say, with probability $Q(Z_1)$, and the probabilities for different integers are statistically independent. This is exactly the same process as that of constructing a random code ensemble for a memoryless channel, except that here the integers are mapped into the Z space by using the Q(Z) measure. Thus we arrive at a set of codes (if there are f letters in the Z alphabet there will be f^{tN} different codes in the ensemble) and each code will have an associated probability. The code in which integer i is mapped into

109

Z_i has probability $\prod\limits_{i=1}^{N} Q(Z_i)$.

We now use Lemma 1 to bound the average distortion for this ensemble of codes (using the probabilities associated with the codes in calculating the average). Note, first, that in the ensemble of codes if $Q(\beta)$ is the Q measure of a set β of Z words, then the probability that this set contains no code words is $[1 - Q(\beta)]^N$, that is, the product of the probability that code word 1 is not in β, that for code word 2, etc. Hence the probability that β contains at least one code word is $1 - [1 - Q(\beta)]^N$. Now, referring to Lemma 1, the average distortion may be bounded by

$$\overline{D} \le \epsilon D_{max} + [1 - Q(\beta_M)]^N D_{max} + (D* + \epsilon)$$

Here D_{max} is the largest possible distortion between an m letter and a z letter. The first term, ϵD_{max}, arises from message words M which are not in the set α. These have total probability less than or equal to ϵ and, when they occur, average distortion less than or equal to D_{max}. The second term overbounds the contribution that is due to cases in which the set β_M for the message M does not contain at least one code word. The probability of this in the ensemble is certainly bounded by $[1 - Q(\beta_M)]^N$, and the distortion is necessarily bounded by D_{max}. Finally, if the message is in α and there is at least one code word in β_M, the distortion is bounded by $D* + \epsilon$, according to Lemma 1. Now, $Q(\beta_M) \ge e^{-t[R(D*)+\epsilon]}$. Also, for $0 < x \le 1$,

$$(1-x)^{\frac{1}{x}} = e^{\frac{1}{x}\log(1-x)} \le e^{\frac{1}{x}\left(-x+\frac{x^2}{2}\right)} = e^{-1+\frac{x}{2}} \le e^{-\frac{1}{2}}$$

(using the alternating and monotonically decreasing nature of the terms of the logarithmic expansion). Hence

$$[1 - Q(\beta_M)]^N \le \left(1 - e^{-t[R(D*)+\epsilon]}\right)^N$$

$$= \left[1 - e^{-t[R(D*)+\epsilon]}\right]^{e^{t[R(D*)+\epsilon]} e^{-t[R(D*)+\epsilon]}N} \le e^{-\frac{1}{2}e^{-t[R(D*)+\epsilon]}N}$$

If we choose for N, the number of points, the value $e^{t[R(D*)+2\epsilon]}$ (or, if this is not an integer, the smallest integer exceeding this quantity), then the expression given above is bounded by $e^{-\frac{1}{2}e^{t\epsilon}}$. Thus the average distortion is bounded with this choice of N by

$$\overline{D} \le \epsilon D_{max} + e^{-\frac{1}{2}e^{t\epsilon}} D_{max} + D* + \epsilon$$

$$\le D* + \delta$$

provided that ϵ in Lemma 1 is chosen small enough to make $\epsilon (D_{max} + 1) \le \delta/2$ and then t is chosen large enough to make $e^{-\frac{1}{2}e^{t\epsilon}} D_{max} \le \frac{\delta}{2}$. We also require that ϵ be small enough and t large enough to make N, the integer just greater than or equal to $e^{t[R(D*) + 2\epsilon]}$, less than or equal to $e^{t[R(D*) + \delta]}$. Since Lemma 1 holds for all sufficiently large t and any positive ϵ , these can all be simultaneously satisfied.

We have shown, then, that the conditions of the theorem are satisfied by the average distortion of the ensemble of codes. It follows that there exists at least one specific code in the ensemble whose average distortion is bounded by $D*+ \delta$. This concludes the proof.

Corollary. Theorem 2 remains true if δ is replaced by 0 in property (1). It also remains true if the δ in property (1) is retained and the δ in property (2) is replaced by 0, provided in this case that $D* > D_{min}$, the smallest D for which R(D) is defined.

This corollary asserts that we can attain (or do better than) one coordinate of the R(D) curve and approximate, as closely as desired, the other, except possibly for the D_{min} point. To prove the first statement of the corollary, note first that it is true for $D* \geq D_{max}$, the value for which $R(D_{max}) = 0$. Indeed, we may achieve the point $\overline{D} = D_{max}$ with N = 1 and a code of length 1, using only the Z word consisting of the single Z letter which gives this point of the curve. For $D_{min} \leq D* < D_{max}$, apply Theorem 2 to approximate $D** = D* + \frac{\delta}{2}$. Since the curve is strictly decreasing, this approximation will lead to codes with $\overline{D} \leq D*+ \delta$ and $\frac{1}{t} \log N \leq R(D*)$, if the δ in Theorem 2 is made sufficiently small.

The second simplification in the corollary is carried out in a similar fashion, by choosing a $D**$ slightly smaller than the desired $D*$ — that is, a $D**$ such that $R(D**) = R(D*) + \frac{\delta}{2}$, and by using Theorem 2 to approximate this point of the curve.

Now suppose we have a memoryless channel of capacity C. By the coding theorem for such channels it is possible to construct codes and decoding systems with rate approximating C (per use of the channel) and error probability $\leq \epsilon_1$ for any $\epsilon_1 > 0$. We may combine such a code for a channel with a code of the type mentioned above for a source at a given distortion level $D*$ and obtain the following result.

Theorem 3. Given a source characterized by R(D) and a memoryless channel with capacity C > 0, given $\epsilon > 0$ and $D* > D_{min}$, there exists, for sufficiently large t and n, a block code that maps source words of length t into channel input words of length n and a decoding system that maps channel output words of length n into reproduced words of length t and satisfying

111

1) $\bar{D} \leqslant D^*$

2) $\dfrac{nC}{t} \leqslant R(D^*) + \epsilon$

Thus we may find codes with average distortion level as good or better than any desired D^* (greater than D_{min}) and at the same time approximate using the channel at a rate corresponding to $R(D^*)$. This is done, as in the corollary stated above, by approximating the R(D) curve slightly to the left of D^*, say, at $R(D^*) - \delta$. Such a code will have $N = e^{t[R(D^* - \delta) + \delta_1]}$ words, where δ_1 can be made small by taking t large. Next, a code for the channel is constructed with N words and of length n, the largest integer satisfying $\dfrac{nC}{t} \leqslant R(D^* - \delta) + \delta_1$. By choosing t sufficiently large, this will approach zero error probability, since it corresponds to a rate less than channel capacity. If these two codes are combined, it produces an over-all code with average distortion $\leqslant D^*$.

Numerical Results for Some Simple Channels

In this section some numerical results will be given for certain simple channels and sources. Consider, first, a binary independent letter source with equiprobable letters and suppose that the distortion measure is the error probability (per letter). This falls into the class for which a simple explicit solution was given. The R(D) curve, in fact, is

$$R(D) = 1 + D \log_2 D + (1 - D) \log_2 (1 - D) \qquad \text{(bits per source letter)}$$

This, of course, is the same formula as that for the capacity of a symmetric binary channel with probabilities D and (1 - D), the reason being that these constitute the probability assignment $q_i(j)$ which solves the minimizing problem.

This R(D) curve is shown in Fig. 5. Our coding results interpreted here say, for example, that to transmit this source over a channel with error probability .1 requires a channel capacity of at least .56 bits per digit transmitted and if the channel capacity available is this large, codes can be constructed which will approach this error rate. If an error probability of .3 can be tolerated, a capacity of only about .1 bit is necessary and sufficient. If .5 error probability can be tolerated, of course no channel capacity is required. Indeed, one might write down at the receiving point a series of zeroes.

Also plotted in Fig. 5 are a number of points corresponding to specific simple codes where we have assumed a noiseless binary channel is available. A particular code is

112

represented by a point whose abscissa is the error probability for the code and whose ordinate is the channel capacity used per message letter. All points must therefore lie on or above the R(D) curve and their distance above is a measure of how closely they approximate ideal encoding.

One point, D = 0, is obtained with capacity 1 bit per message letter simply by sending the binary digits through the channel. Other simple codes which encode 3, 5, 7, and 9 message letters into one channel letter are the following. For the ratio 5, for example, encode message sequences of five digits into 0 or 1 accordingly as the sequence contains more than half zeros or more than half ones.

At the receiving point, a 0 is decoded into a sequence of zeros of the appropriate length and a 1 into a sequence of ones. These rather degenerate codes are plotted in Fig. 5 with crosses. Simple though they are, with block length of the channel sequences only one, they still approximate to some extent the lower bound.

Plotted on the same curve are solid points corresponding to the well-known single-error correcting codes [2] with block lengths 3, 5, 7, 15, and 31. These codes are used backwards here - any message in the 15-dimensional cube, for example, is transmitted over the channel as what would ordinarily be the eleven message digits of its nearest code point. At the receiving point, the corresponding fifteen-digit message is reconstructed. This can differ at most in one place from the original message. Thus for this case the ratio of channel to message letters is $\frac{11}{15}$, and the error probability is easily found to be $\frac{1}{16}$. This series of points gives an approximation to the lower bound for lower values of D.

It is possible to fill in densely between points of these discrete series by a technique of mixing codes. For example, one may alternate in using two codes. More generally, one may mix them in proportions λ and $1 - \lambda$, where λ is any rational fraction. Such a mixture gives a code with a new ratio R of channel to message letters, given by $R = \lambda R_1 + (1 - \lambda)R_2$, where R_1 and R_2 are the ratios for the given codes, and with new error probability $P_e = \lambda P_{e_1} + (1 - \lambda)P_{e_2}$. This gives a linear interpolation between any two code points. For example, when applied to two of the simple codes in Fig. 5, it produced the series of points indicated by open circles. This mixing technique may be applied in any case of a single-letter distortion measure to give a linear interpolation between two known codes. It may also be used to give an alternative

113

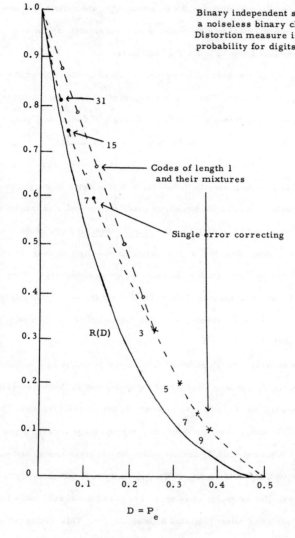

Binary independent source coded into a noiseless binary channel. Distortion measure is error probability for digits.

Codes of length 1 and their mixtures

Single error correcting

R(D)

Fig. 5

114

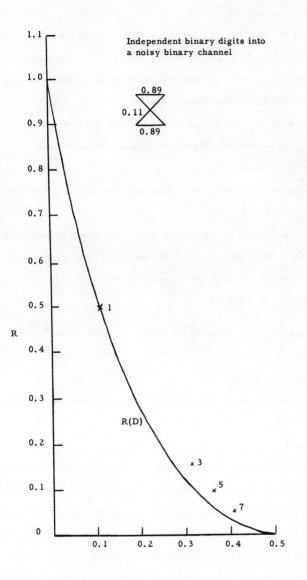

Fig. 6

proof of the convexity of the R(D) curve.

Another channel was also studied with regard to actual codes, namely, the binary symmetric channel of capacity $C = \frac{1}{2}$. This has probabilities 0.89 that a digit is received correctly and 0.11 incorrectly. Here the series of points (Fig. 6) for simple codes actually touches the lower bound at the point $R = \frac{1}{2}$. This is because the channel itself, without coding, produces just this error probability. Any symmetric binary channel will have one point that can be attained exactly by means of straight transmission, when error probability is the distortion measure.

Figure 7 shows the R(D) curve for another simple situation, a binary independent letter source but with the reproduced Z alphabet consisting of three letters, 0, 1, and ?. The distortion measure is zero for a correct digit, one for an incorrect digit, and 0.25 for ?. In the same figure is shown, for comparison, the R(D) curve without the ? option.

Figure 8 shows the R(D) curves for independent letter sources with various numbers of equiprobable letters in the alphabet (2, 3, 4, 5, 10, 100). Here again the distortion measure is taken to be error probability (for a reproduced digit). With b letters in the alphabet the R(D, b) curve is given by

$$R(D,b) = \begin{cases} \log_2 b + D \log_2 \dfrac{D}{b-1} + (1-D) \log_2 (1-D) & D \leq \dfrac{b-1}{b} \\ 0 & D > \dfrac{b-1}{b} \end{cases}$$

Generalization to Continuous Cases

We will now sketch briefly a generalization of the single-letter distortion measure to cases where the input and output alphabets are not restricted to finite sets but vary over arbitrary spaces.

Assume a message alphabet $A = \{m\}$ and a reproduced letter alphabet $B = \{z\}$. For each pair (m, z) in these alphabets let $d(m, z)$ be a non-negative number, the distortion if m is reproduced as z. Further, we assume a probability measure P defined over a Borel field of subsets of the A space. Finally, we require that, for each z belonging to B, $d(m, z)$ is a measurable function with finite expectation.

Consider a finite selection of points $z_i (i = 1, 2, \ldots, \mathcal{L})$ from the B space, and a measurable assignment of transition probabilities $q(z_i | m)$. (That is, for each i, $q(z_i | m)$ is a measurable function in the A space.) For such a choice of z_i and assign-

116

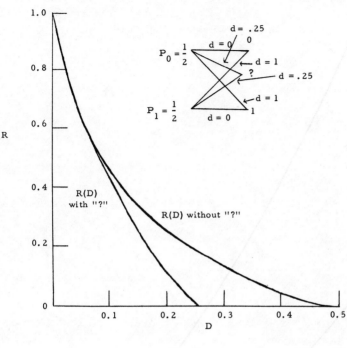

Fig. 7

ment $q(z_i|m)$, a mutual information and an average distortion are determined.

$$R = \sum_i \int_A q(z_i|m) \log \frac{q(z_i|m)}{\int q(z_i|m) \, dP(m)} \, dP(m)$$

$$D = \sum_i \int_A d(m, z_i) \, q(z_i|m) \, dP(m)$$

We define the rate distortion function $R(D^*)$ for such a case as the greatest lower bound of R when the set of points z_i is varied (both in choice and number) and the $q(z_i|m)$ is varied over measurable transition probabilities, subject to keeping the distortion at the level D^* or less.

Most of the results we have found for the finite alphabet case carry through easily under this generalization. In particular, the convexity property of the $R(D)$ curve still holds. In fact, if $R(D)$ can be approximated to within ϵ by a choice z_i and $q(z_i|m)$ and

117

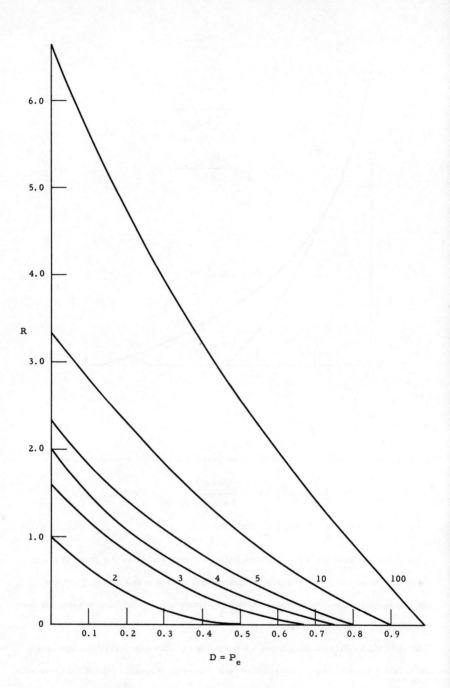

Fig. 8

118

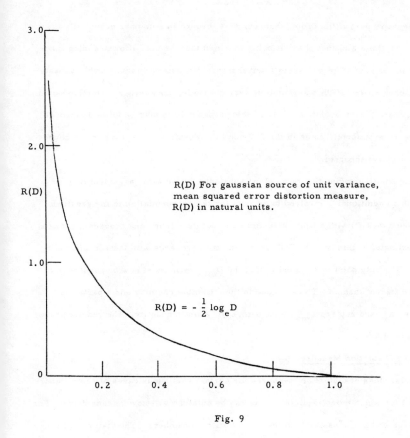

R(D) For gaussian source of unit variance, mean squared error distortion measure, R(D) in natural units.

$$R(D) = -\frac{1}{2} \log_e D$$

Fig. 9

R(D') by a choice z_i' and $q'(z_i'|m)$, then one considers the choice z_i'' consisting of the union of the points z_i and z_i', together with $q''(z_i''|m) = \frac{1}{2} [q(z_i''|m) + q'(z_i''|m)]$, (using zero if $q(z''|m)$ or $q'(z''|m)$ is undefined). This leads, by the convexity of R and by the linearity of D, to an assignment for $D'' = \frac{1}{2} D + \frac{1}{2} D'$, giving an R'' within ϵ of the midpoint of the line joining (D, R(D)) and (D', R(D')). It follows, since ϵ can be made arbitrarily small, that the greatest lower bound of R(D'') is on or below this midpoint.

In the general case it is, however, not necessarily true that the R(D) curve approaches a finite end-point when D decreases toward its minimum possible value. The behavior may be as indicated in Fig. 9 with R(D) going to infinity as D goes to D_{min}. On the other hand, under the conditions we have stated, there is a finite D_{max} for which $R(D_{max}) = 0$. This value of D is given by

119

$$D_{max} = g.\ell.b.\ \underset{z}{E}\ [\ d(m, z)]$$

The negative part of the coding theorem goes through in a manner essentially the same as the finite alphabet case, it being assumed that the only allowed coding functions from the source sequences to channel inputs correspond to measurable subsets of the source space. (If this assumption were not made, the average distortion would not, in general, even be defined.) The various inequalities may be followed through, changing the appropriate sums in the A space to integrals and resulting in the corresponding negative theorem.

For the positive coding theorem, also, substantially the same argument may be used with an additional ϵ involved to account for the approximation to the greatest lower bound of R(D) with a finite selection of z_i points. Thus, one chooses a set of z_i to approximate, within ϵ, the R(D) curve and then proceeds with the random coding method. The only point to be noted is that the D_{max} term must now be handled in a slightly different fashion. To each code in the ensemble one may add a particular point, say z_o, and replace D_{max} by $E(d(m, z_o))$, a finite quantity. The results of the theorem then follow.

Difference Distortion Measure

A special class of distortion measures for certain continuous cases of some importance and for which more explicit results can be obtained will now be considered. For these the m and z spaces are both the sets of all real numbers. The distortion measure d(m, z) will be called a <u>difference distortion measure</u> if it is a function only of the difference m - z, thus d(m, z) = e(m - z). A common example is the squared error measure, $d(m, z) = (m - z)^2$ or, again, the absolute error criterion $d(m, z) = |m - z|$.

We will develop a lower bound on R(D) for a difference distortion measure. First we define a function $\phi(D)$ for a given difference measure e(u) as follows. Consider an arbitrary distribution function G(u) and let H be its entropy and D the average distortion between a random variable with the given distribution and zero. Thus

$$H = - \int_{-\infty}^{\infty} \log \frac{dG(u)}{du}\ dG(u)$$

$$d = \int_{-\infty}^{\infty} e(u)\ dG(u)$$

We wish to vary the distribution $G(u)$, keeping $D \leqslant D^*$ and seek the maximum H. The least upper bound, if finite, is clearly actually attained as a maximum for some distribution. This maximum H for a given D^* we call $\phi(D^*)$, and a corresponding distribution function is called a maximizing distribution for this D^*.

Now suppose we have a distribution function for the m space (generalized letter probabilities) $P(m)$, with entropy $H(m)$. We wish to show that

$$R(D) \geqslant H(m) - \phi(D)$$

Let z_i be a set of z points and $q(z_i | m)$ an assignment of transition probabilities. Then the mutual information between m and z may be written

$$R = H(m) - \sum_i Q_i H(m | z_i)$$

where Q_i is the resulting probability of z_i. If we let D_i be the average distortion between m and z_i, then

$$H(m | z_i) \leqslant \phi(D_i)$$

This is because $\phi(D)$ was the maximum H for a given average distortion and also because the distortion is a function only of the difference between m and z, so that this maximizing value applies for any z_i. Thus

$$R \geqslant H(m) - \sum_i Q_i \phi(D_i)$$

Now $\phi(D)$ is a concave function. This is a consequence of the concavity of entropy considered as a function of a distribution function and the linearity of D in the same space of distribution functions, by an argument identical with that used previously. Hence, $\sum_i Q_i \phi(D_i) \leqslant \phi(\sum_i Q_i D_i) = \phi(D)$, where D is the average distortion with the choice z_i and the assigned transition probabilities. It follows that

$$R \geqslant H(m) - \phi(D)$$

Since this is true for any assignment z_i and $q(z_i | m)$ the desired result is proved.

If, for a particular $P(m)$ and $e(u)$, assignments can be made which approach arbitrarily close to this lower bound, then, of course, this is the R(D) function. Such is the case, for example, if $P(m)$ is gaussian and $e(u) = u^2$ (mean square error measure of distortion). Suppose that the message has variance σ^2, and consider a gaussian distribution of mean zero and variance $\sigma^2 - D$ in the z space. (If this is zero or negative, clearly $R(D) = 0$ by using only the z point zero.) Let the conditional probabilities

121

$q(m|z)$ be gaussian with variance D. This is consistent with the gaussian character of $P(m)$, since normal distributions convolve to give normal distributions with the sum of the individual variances. These assignments determine the conditional probability measure $q(z|m)$, also then normal.

A simple calculation shows that this assignment attains the lower bound given above. The resulting R(D) curve is

$$R(D) = \begin{cases} \log \dfrac{\sigma}{\sqrt{D}} & D \leq \sigma^2 \\[2ex] 0 & D > \sigma^2 \end{cases}$$

This is shown for $\sigma^2 = 1$ in Fig. 9.

Definition of a Local Distortion Measure

Thus far we have considered only a distortion measure d_{ij} (or $d(m,z)$) which depends upon comparison of a message letter with the corresponding reproduced letter, this letter-to-letter distortion to be averaged over the length of message and over the set of possible messages and possible reproduced messages. In many practical cases, however, this type of measure is not sufficiently general. The seriousness of a particular type of error often depends on the context.

Thus in transmitting a stock market quotation, say: "A.T.& T. 5900 shares, closing 194," an error in the 9 of 5900 shares would normally be much less serious than an error in the 9 of the closing price.

We shall now consider a distortion measure that depends upon local context and, in fact, compares blocks of g message letters with the corresponding blocks of g letters of the reproduced message.

A local distortion measure of span g is a function $d(m_1, m_2, \ldots, m_g; z_1, z_2, \ldots, z_g)$ of message sequences of length g and reproduced message sequences of length g (from a possibly different or larger alphabet) with the property that $d \geq 0$. The distortion between $M = m_1, m_2, \ldots, m_t$ and $Z = z_1, z_2, \ldots, z_t$ $(t \geq g)$ is defined by

$$D(M, Z) = \frac{1}{t - g + 1} \sum_{k=1}^{t-g+1} d(m_k, m_{k+1}, \ldots, m_{k+g-1}; z_k, z_{k+1}, \ldots, z_{k+g-1})$$

The distortion of a block code in which message M and reproduced version Z occur with probability $P(M, Z)$ is defined by

$$d = \sum_{M, Z} P(M, Z) D(M, Z).$$

122

In other words, we assume, with a local distortion measure, that the evaluation of an entire system is obtained by averaging the distortions for all block comparisons of length g each with its probability of occurrence a weighting factor.

The Functions $R_n(D)$ and $R(D)$ for a Local Distortion Measure and Ergodic Source

Assume that we have given an ergodic message source and a local distortion measure. Consider blocks of n message letters with their associated probabilities (as determined by the source) together with possible blocks Z of reproduced message of length n. Let an arbitrary assignment of transition probabilities from the M blocks to the Z blocks, $q(Z|M)$, be made. For this assignment we can calculate two quantities: 1) the average mutual information per letter $R = \frac{1}{n} E\left(\log \frac{q(Z|M)}{Q(Z)}\right)$ and 2) the average distortion if the M's were reproduced as Z's with the probabilities $q(Z|M)$. This is $D = \sum_{M, Z} P(M, Z)D(M, Z)$. By variation of $q(Z|M)$, while holding $D \leqslant D^*$, we can, in principle, find the minimum R for each D^*. This we call $R_n(D^*)$.

The minimizing problem here is identical with that discussed previously if we think of M and Z as individual letters in a (large) alphabet, and various results relating to this minimum can be applied. In particular, $R_n(D)$ is a convex downward function.

We now define the <u>rate distortion function</u> for the given source relative to the distortion measure as

$$R(D) = \lim_{n \to \infty} \inf R_n(D) .$$

It can be shown, by a direct but tedious argument which we shall omit, that the "inf" may be deleted from this definition. In other words, $R_n(D)$ approaches a limit as $n \to \infty$.

We are now in a position to prove coding theorems for a general ergodic source with a local distortion measure.

The Positive Coding Theorem for a Local Distortion Measure

<u>Theorem 4.</u> Suppose that we are given an ergodic source and a local distortion measure of span g with rate distortion function R(D). Let K be a memoryless discrete channel with capacity C, let D^* be a value of distortion, and let ϵ be a positive number. Then there exists a block code with distortion less than or equal to $D^* + \epsilon$, and with a signaling rate at least ($\frac{C}{R(D^*)}$ - ϵ) message letters per channel letter.

<u>Proof.</u> Choose an n_1 so that $R_{n_1}(D^*) - R(D^*) < \frac{\epsilon}{3}$ and, also, so large that

$\frac{g}{n_1} D_{max} < \frac{\epsilon}{3}$. Now consider blocks of length n_1 as "letters" of an enlarged alphabet.

Using Theorem 3 we can construct a block code using sufficiently long sequences of these "letters" signaling at a rate close to (say within $\epsilon/3$ of) $R_{n_1}(D^*)/C$ (in terms of original message letters) and with distortion less than $D^* + \frac{\epsilon}{3}$. It must be remembered that this distortion is based on a single "letter" comparison. However, the distortion by the given local distortion measure will differ from this only because of overlap comparisons (g for each n_1 letters of message) and hence the discrepancy is, at most, $\frac{g}{n_1} D_{max} < \frac{\epsilon}{3}$. It follows that this code signals at a rate within ϵ of $R(D^*)$ and at a distortion within ϵ of D^*.

The Converse Coding Theorem

Theorem 5. Suppose that we are given an ergodic source and a local distortion measure with rate distortion function $R(D)$. Let K be a memoryless discrete channel with capacity C, let D^* be a value of distortion, and let ϵ be a positive number. Then there exists t_o which is such that any code transmitting $t \geq t_o$ message letters with n uses of the channel at distortion D^*, or less, satisfies

$$\frac{n}{t} C \geq R(D^*) - \epsilon .$$

That is, the channel capacity bits used per message letter must be nearly $R(D^*)$ for long transmissions.

Proof. Choose t_o so that for $t \geq t_o$ we have $R_t(D) \geq R(D) - \epsilon$. Since $R(D)$ was defined as $\lim_{t \to \infty} \inf R_t(D)$, this is possible. Suppose that we have a code for such a $t \geq t_o$ which maps sequences M consisting of t message letters into sequences X of n channel letters and decodes sequences Y of n channel output letters into sequences Z of reproduced messages. The channel will have, from its transition probabilities, some $P(Y|X)$. Furthermore, from the encoding and decoding functions, we shall have $X = f(M)$ and $Z = g(Y)$. Finally, there will be, from the source, probabilities for the message sequences $P(M)$. Due to the encoding function $f(M)$ this will induce a set of probabilities $P(X)$ for input sequences. If the channel capacity is C, the average mutual information $R(X, Y)$ between input and output sequences must satisfy

$$R(X, Y) = E \log \frac{P(X|Y)}{P(X)} \leq nC$$

since nC is the maximum possible value of this quantity when $P(X)$ is varied. Also, since X is a function of M and Z is a function of Y, we have

124

$$R(M, Z) = E \log \frac{P(M \mid Z)}{P(M)} \leq R(X, Y) \leq nC$$

The coding system in question amounts, over-all, to a set of conditional probabilities from M sequences to Z sequences as determined by the two coding functions and the transition probabilities. If the distortion of the over-all system is less than or equal to D^*, then $tR_t(D^*) = \min\limits_{P(Z \mid M)} R(M, Z)$ is certainly less than or equal to the particular R(M, Z) obtained with the probabilities given by the channel and coding system. $(R_t(D^*)$ is multiplied by t because $R_t(D)$ is measured on a per message letter basis, while the R(M, Z) quantities are for sequences of length t.) Thus

$$tR_t(D^*) \leq R(M, Z) \leq nC$$

$$t(R(D^*) - \epsilon) \leq nC$$

$$\frac{n}{t} C \geq R(D^*) - \epsilon$$

This is the conclusion of the theorem.

Notice from the method of proof that the code used again need not be a block code, provided only that after n uses of the channel t recovered letters are written down. If one has some kind of variable-length code and, starting at time zero, uses this code continually, the inequality of the theorem will hold for any finite time after t_0 message letters have been recovered; and of course as longer and longer blocks are compared, $\epsilon \to 0$. It is even possible to generalize this to variable-length codes in which, after n uses of the channel, the number of recovered message letters is a random variable depending, perhaps, on the particular message and the particular chance operation of the channel. If, as is usually the case in such codes, there exists an average signaling rate with the properties that after n uses of the channel then, with probability nearly one, t letters will be written down, with t lying between $t_1(1 - \delta)$ and $t_1(1 + \delta)$ (the $\delta \to 0$ as $n \to \infty$), then essentially the same theorem applies, using the mean t_1 for t.

Channels with Memory

Finally, we mention that while we have, in the above discussion, assumed the channel to be memoryless, very similar results, both of positive and negative type, can be obtained for channels with memory.

For a channel with memory one may define a capacity C_n for the first n uses of the channel starting at state s_0. This C_n is $\frac{1}{n}$ times the maximum average mutual information between input sequences of length n and resulting output sequences when the probabilities assigned the input sequences of length n are varied. The lower bound on distortion after n uses of the channel is that given by Theorem 1 using C_n for C.

We can also define the capacity C for such a channel as $C = \lim_{n \to \infty} \sup C_n$. The positive parts of the theorem then state that one can find arbitrarily long block codes satisfying Theorem 3. In most channels of interest, of course, historical influences die out in such a way as to make $C_n \to C$ as $n \to \infty$. For memoryless channels, $C_n \equiv C$ for all n.

Duality of a Source and a Channel

There is a curious and provocative duality between the properties of a source with a distortion measure and those of a channel. This duality is enhanced if we consider channels in which there is a "cost" associated with the different input letters, and it is desired to find the capacity subject to the constraint that the expected cost not exceed a certain quantity. Thus input letter i might have cost v_i and we wish to find the capacity with the side condition $\sum_i P_i v_i \leqslant v$, say, where P_i is the probability of using input letter i. This problem amounts, mathematically, to <u>maximizing</u> a mutual information under variation of the P_i with a linear inequality as constraint. The solution of this problem leads to a capacity cost function C(v) for the channel. It can be shown readily that this function is <u>concave</u> downward. Solving this problem corresponds, in a sense, to finding a source that is just right for the channel and the desired cost.

In a somewhat dual way, evaluating the rate distortion function R(D) for a source amounts , mathematically, to <u>minimizing</u> a mutual information under variation of the $q_i(j)$, again with a linear inequality as constraint. The solution leads to a function R(D) which is <u>convex</u> downward. Solving this problem corresponds to finding a channel that is just right for the source and allowed distortion level. This duality can be pursued further and is related to a duality between past and future and the notions of control and knowledge. Thus, we may have knowledge of the past but cannot control it; we may control the future but have no knowledge of it.

BIBLIOGRAPHY

[1] C.E. Shannon and W. Weaver, The Mathematical Theory of Communication, University of Illinois Press, 1949.

[2] R.W. Hamming, "Error-Detecting and Error-Correcting Codes, " <u>Bell System Technical Journal</u>, Vol. 29, 1950, p. 147.

GROUP TESTING TO CLASSIFY EFFICIENTLY ALL UNITS IN A BINOMIAL SAMPLE

Milton Sobel

1. Summary.

A number N of units are to be classified as good or defective by means of "group-tests." A "group-test" is a simultaneous test on x units with only two possible outcomes: "success" indicating that all x units are good and "failure" indicating that at least one of the x units is defective (we don't know how many or which ones). The problem is to find a simple and efficient procedure or to find the most efficient procedure for classifying each of the N units as good or defective. For finite N, efficiency is defined in the sense of minimizing the expected number of group-tests required; for infinite N, efficiency is defined in the sense of maximizing the expected number of units classified per test in the long run as the number of tests increases.

At the outset any set of units is assumed to be a random sample of independent observations from a binomial distribution with a common known a priori probability q of a unit being good and p = 1-q of being defective.

A simple procedure (or decision rule) R_1, which describes a mode of action for any given value of q, is proposed and compared with other procedures for the same problem. Explicit instructions for carrying out R_1 are given in [4] for values of N from 1 to 16 for all q and for values of N from 17 to 100 for q = .90, .95 and .99. Section 14 gives for any N and any q an alternative way of carrying out R_1 which does not require the computation of special tables. Exact formulas and numerical results for the expected number of group-tests required are given in [4] and some of the latter are repeated in Table II below; two lower bounds are described in Section 12 with numerical values given in Table II.

Technical applications, other than the known application to blood testing, and some conjectures on optimality are given, in Section 2.

Several different generalizations of the problem are mentioned in Section 11; detailed formulas are given in [4].

To show that R_1 is not generally optimal in the finite case, a modification R_0 of R_1 is defined in Section 13 and its improvement over R_1 is shown in Table II.

Another procedure R_2, which is simpler to compute and is related to R_1 in several ways, is defined in Section 15 in terms of information theory concepts. A "halving" procedure R_4 is also defined for purposes of comparison; numerical comparisons are given in [4] for the finite case and in Table I below for the infinite case.

A good deal of this paper is a restatement without proofs of results proved in [4] and of conjectures first stated in [4] . Much of Sections 6, 12, 13, and 14 is new material.

2. Introduction.

A problem which has hitherto been considered only in connection with blood-testing applications [1] , [2], [5] is shown to have industrial applications, and these have focused interest on a more general treatment of the problem. During World War II a great saving was accomplished in the field of blood testing by pooling a fixed number of blood samples and testing the pooled sample for some particular disease. If the disease was not present, then several people were passed by a single test; if the disease was present, then there was enough blood remaining in each blood sample to test each one separately. The amount of time, money, and effort saved by such a procedure depends on how rare this disease is in the population of people being tested. In this application the total number of people to be tested was regarded as unknown and very large.

The goal of the problem treated here is the same, namely to separate the defective units from the good units with a minimal (or approximately minimal) number of group-tests. The main problem treated here is a generalization of that above in the following respects:

i) The population size N (number of people to be tested above) is finite and known at the outset. The case N = ∞ is briefly discussed in Section 6.

ii) The number of units in each group-test (pooled blood samples above) is not necessarily constant. Actually this is a consequence of i) since the size of the next group-test cannot be greater than the number of units not yet classified.

iii) If a group-test fails (at least one defective - or in the context above, at least one diseased sample - is present) then we do not necessarily test each item separately.

128

In practice the simplicity of the procedure deserves some consideration. The proposed procedure R_1 defined in Section 3, after having been computed and described explicitly in advance of any experimentation, is in some sense no more complicated than the blood-testing procedure described above; this is explained in Section 5.

Some typical industrial applications are the following; in each case the a priori probability q of a unit being good is assumed to be given.

1. It is desired to remove all "leakers" from a set of N devices. One chemical apparatus is available and the devices are tested by putting x of them (where $1 \leq x \leq N$) in a bell jar and testing whether any of the gas used in constructing the devices has leaked out into the bell jar. It is assumed that the presence of gas in the bell jar indicates only that there is at least one leaker and that the amount of gas gives no indication of the number of leakers.

2. Paper capacitors are tested at most N at a time and each test indicates by the presence (or absence) of a current that there is at least one defective (or no defectives) present. For given N and given cost of unit manufacture, should the operator throw away a whole set of N units if it contains at least one defective? If not, how should he proceed to sort out the defective units to minimize the expected number of tests required? If the cost of a group-test and the cost of producing a unit are known then a related problem is to find a procedure which minimizes the total cost (including testing costs) of producing a good unit.

3. Christmas Tree Lighting Problem: A batch of N light bulbs are electrically arranged in series and tested by applying a voltage across the whole batch or any subset thereof. If this is to be done on a routine basis, what procedure should be used to minimize the expected number of tests required to remove all the defective light bulbs, assuming the value of q is given?

4. A test indicates whether or not there is at least one good unit present in a batch of N, without indicating which ones or how many are good. What procedure should be used to find all the good units? This problem is dual to those above. For example, if the probability that a fuse is faulty is very low, one could test many fuses in series for continuity, as in the Christmas tree problem; but if the same probability is very high, one could test many fuses in parallel for continuity. The identical analysis applies, mutatis mutandis.

129

A procedure, R_1, which describes for each value of q a sequence of tests leading to the classification of each of the N units as good or defective, is proposed and compared with several other procedures applicable to the same problem. The procedure R_1 is simple in the sense that between any two successive tests, i) future tests are concerned only with units not yet classified as good or defective, ii) units not yet classified have to be separated into only (at most) two sets, and iii) the units within each set need not be distinguishable.

1. Based on the assumption that at any stage the next group for testing is taken from only one of these two sets (and is not formed by mixing together units from both sets), the procedure R_1 is shown below to be optimal for all values of q.

2. If it is given that the units are never distinguishable from one another (except as they are indicated to be good or defective) - i.e., that it is impossible or economically impractical to identify individual units - then the procedure R_1 is conjectured to be optimal for all q.

3. In some applications the units are linearly arranged in fixed positions and tests can only be carried out on an "interval" of successive units. The procedure R_1 can be applied to such problems and it is conjectured to be optimal for all q.

4. Although the procedure R_1 depends on the given finite value of N, a natural modification R_{21} of R_1 can be applied when units continue indefinitely to arrive on an assembly line basis, i.e., when $N = \infty$. In this case every unit must be classified in a finite number of steps. If we consider the limit as $T \rightarrow \infty$ of the expectation of the ratio of the number of units classified in T tests to T as a criterion for efficiency, then R_{21} is conjectured to be optimal for all q. This discussion is amplified in Section 6 below.

5. Finally, it is conjectured that, for $q < (1 + \sqrt{33})/8 \doteq .843$, the procedure R_1 is optimal for any finite N.

For finite N, another procedure R_0 is described which is identical with R_1 for $q < .843$ and is an improvement over R_1 for $q > .843$; however the procedure R_0 is also more complicated than R_1. The procedure R_0 is optimal for all q if N is very small; it is not known whether or to what extent this property remains true for intermediate and large values of N.

Among several other procedures defined for purposes of comparison with R_1, one of

130

these, called R_2, is simpler to compute explicitly. It is defined in Section 15 in terms of information theory concepts. Another procedure, R_4, is a "halving procedure" which starts by testing all the N units and, if a defective is present, the next test is carried out on $N/2$ or $(N-1)/2$ items which are chosen at random. This procedure has the advantage that it can be carried out without knowing the true value of q.

Several different directions for generalization of the basic problem and corresponding generalizations of the procedure R_1 are considered in Section 11.

3. The Procedure R_1

The procedure R_1 will be defined implicitly by a pair of recursion formulas and simple boundary conditions after some definitions and preliminary results. In the course of experimentation under R_1, the units proven good and the units proven defective are never[1] used in subsequent tests. Aside from such units, the procedure R_1 requires that between any two successive tests the remaining (or unclassified) units of number $n \leq N$ be separated into at most two sets. One set of size $m \geq 0$, called the "defective set, " is known to contain at least one defective unit if $m \geq 1$; (it is not known which ones are defective nor exactly how many there are.) The other set of size $n - m \geq 0$ is called the "binomial set" because we have no knowledge about it other than the original binomial assumptions, i.e., given the past history of testing, the a posteriori distribution associated with these units is that of independent binomial chance variables with a common probability q of being good. Either of these two sets can be empty in the course of experimentation; both are empty at termination.

For a defective set of size $m \geq 1$ the (conditional) probability that the number of defective units Y present equals y is

(1) $$P\left\{ Y = y \mid Y \geq 1 \right\} = \frac{\binom{m}{y} p^y q^{m-y}}{1 - q^m} \qquad (y = 1, 2, \ldots, m).$$

If Z denotes the number of defectives present in a subset of size x (with $1 \leq x < m$) randomly chosen from the defective set, then

(2) $$P\left\{ Z = 0 \mid Y \geq 1 \right\} = \sum_{y=1}^{m-x} \frac{\binom{m}{y} p^y q^{m-y}}{1 - q^m} \frac{\binom{m-y}{x}}{\binom{m}{x}} = \frac{q^x(1-q^{m-x})}{1 - q^m} .$$

The following simple result, which is a special case of a lemma proved in [4] ,

_____

[1] In certain classical weighing problems with a known number of defectives, involving a pan balance, such units are used in subsequent tests.

plays a fundamental role in the derivation of R_1 below.

Lemma 1: Given a defective set of size $m > 1$, and given that a proper subset of size x with $1 \leq x < m$ also proves to contain at least one defective, then the a posteriori distribution associated with the $m - x$ remaining units is precisely that of $m - x$ independent binomial chance variables with the common probability q of being good.

As a result of the above lemma we can test proper subsets of a defective set and be assured that, regardless of the outcome, we will always have at most one defective set to work with. This procedure can result in two binomial sets but these can be combined without any loss of "information"; we shall refer to this process of combining binomial sets as "recombination."

Let $E_1\left\{T; m, n, q\right\} = G_1(m, n)$ denote the expected number of group-tests remaining to be performed if the defective set is presently of size m, the binomial set is presently of size $n - m$, the a priori probability of a good unit is the known constant q, and the procedure R_1 is used; for the special case $m = 0$ we use the symbol $E_1\left\{T; n, q\right\} = H_1(n)$. The values of m and n vary as the procedure is carried out; at the outset $m = 0$ and $n = N$. It will also be convenient to refer to the "G-situation" or "G(m, n)-situation" if $m \geq 2$ and to the "H-situation" or "H(n)-situation" if $m = 0$; the case $m = 1 < n$ is immediately reducible to an H-situation without any testing.

Recursion Formulas Defining Procedure R_1.

If x denotes the size of the very next group-test then we write for any H-situation

(3) $$H_1(n) = 1 + \min_{1 \leq x \leq n} \left\{ q^x H_1(n - x) + (1 - q^x) G_1(x, n) \right\}$$

and, for any G-situation, from equation (2) and Lemma 1

(4) $$G_1(m, n) = 1 + \min_{1 \leq x \leq m-1} \left\{ \left(\frac{q^x - q^m}{1 - q^m} \right) G_1(m-x, n-x) + \left(\frac{1 - q^x}{1 - q^m} \right) G_1(x, n) \right\}$$

and the boundary conditions state that for all q

(5) $$H_1(0) = 0 \text{ and } G_1(1, n) = H_1(n-1) \text{ for } n = 1, 2, \ldots .$$

The subscripts in $H_1(n)$, etc. refer to the procedure R_1. In writing (3) and (4) the constant 1 represents the very next group-test of size x and the expression in braces is the conditional expected number of additional group-tests given x. It follows from (3) and (5) that $H_1(1) = 1$ for all q.

Remark 1: To justify writing $G_1(x, n)$ in (4) we make use of Lemma 1 with a defective

132

set of size $m \geq 2$ and a subset of size $x < m$. Then, by Lemma 1, if the subset of size x is shown to contain at least one defective, the a posteriori distribution associated with the remaining $m - x$ units is exactly binomial. These are then mixed or recombined with the $n - m$ "binomial units" giving a total of $n - x$ binomial units.

Remark 2: These two recursion formulas together with the boundary conditions allow one to compute successively for any q the functions $H_1(1)$, $G_1(2,2)$, $H_1(2)$, $G_1(2,3)$, $G_1(3,3)$, $H_1(3)$, $G_1(2,4)$, $G_1(3,4)$, $G_1(4,4)$, $H_1(4)$, ... to any desired value of m and n.

Remark 3: The integer x which accomplishes the minimization in (3) and (4) for each situation characterized by the integers m and n is particularly important since this is the size of the next test to be run according to the procedure R_1. These integers $x = x_1(n;q)$ and $x = x_1(m, n;q)$ define the procedure R_1. An illustration of how the procedure R_1 is to be carried out is given in Section 4. It is pointed out in Section 5 that $x_1(m, n;q)$ depends only on m and q and a procedure for computing it is given there.

Remark 4: If $m \geq 2$ then it is assumed in (4) that a subset of size x with $1 \leq x \leq m$ will be taken from the defective set without mixing them with units from the binomial set. It follows from the expressions (3), (4) and (5) that any lack of optimality can only arise from this "no mixing" assumption. This assumption was used in the derivation of the algorithm (4) (See Remark 1 above). It will be noted in Section 13 that when all the units are individually identified then an improvement to the procedure R_1 for high values of q can be obtained by dropping this assumption. A specific example R_0 of a modification and improvement of the procedure R_1 which drops the "no mixing" assumption at the expense of more complication will be briefly discussed in Section 13.

4. Illustration of the Procedure R_1.

Suppose we start with $N = 12$ units and it is given that $q = .98$. As indicated in the tabulations in [4], the first test-group is of size $x = 12$, i.e., we start by testing all 12 units. If a success occurs the experiment is over; if a failure occurs then, by the tabulations in [4], the next test group is of size $x = 4$ chosen at random from the 12. Similarly we continue along one of the following sample paths.

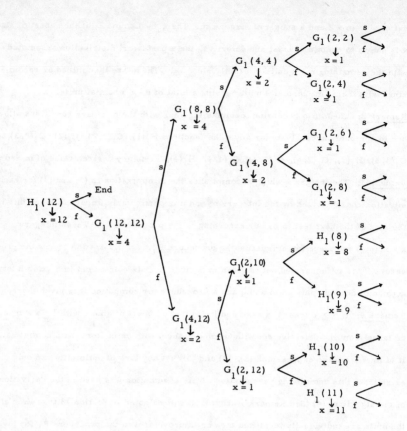

FIG. 1. PARTIAL TREE FOR PROCEDURE R_1 (N = 12, q = .98)

The complete diagram (or "tree") is not shown here but it continues in a similar manner and complete details can be obtained from Figures 3 and 4 of [4].

It is obvious that the above procedure terminates in a finite number of steps. In fact it can be shown for procedure R_1 that the maximum number $M_1(n)$ for any H-situation (or $M_1(m, n)$ for any G-situation) occurs when q is close to unity and the n unclassified units all happen to be defective. It follows easily that

(6) $$M_1(n) = (n + 1)[1 + \alpha(n)] + 1 - 2^{1 + \alpha(n)}$$

(7) $$M_1(m, n) = \alpha(m) + n[1 + \alpha(n-1)] + 1 - 2^{1 + \alpha(n-1)} \qquad (m \geq 2)$$

where $\alpha(n)$ is defined as the positive integer for which

(8) $$2^{\alpha(n)} \leq n < 2^{1 + \alpha(n)}.$$

For the above example $\alpha(12) = 3$ and $M_1(12) = 37$. Although the maximum number is so large, the probability of this maximum is about 10^{-20}, and the expected number of

134

tests for q = 0.98 is only 2.07, with standard deviation about 2.1. A table of probabilities for the number of tests T required with q = .98 and N = 12 is given below:

T	1	2	3	4	5	6	7	8	9	10 - 37
Prob.	.7847	0	0	0	.0801	.1124	.0003	.0016	.0134	.0075

It is interesting to note that if the starting number N is exactly a power of 2 and if q is large then the procedure R_1 starts out, as in [4], exactly the same as a "halving" procedure. Such a halving procedure R_4 is defined in [4] for any N. It has the property that it can be carried out without knowing the true value of q. It is shown in [4] that the procedure R_1 is better than R_4 for $q \geq .844$ and the same result also holds for $q < .844$. For $q \geq .844$, the maximum difference between $E_4(T)$ and $E_1(T)$ occurs at $q = .844$ and is equal to .0379 for $N = 6$, and the procedure R_1 appears to have a variance smaller than that of R_4 for all $q < 1$. A comparison of $E_1(T)$ with $E(T)$ for several other procedures is given in [4].

5. The Simplicity of R_1.

It is pointed out in this section that for any given q and any situation G(m, n) the appropriate x (i.e., the integer which accomplishes the minimization in (4)) does not depend on n. A somewhat simpler method of computing x is given and a new function of m alone is introduced to replace $G_1(m, n)$ in the definition of the procedure R_1. For any $m \geq 2$ and any pair of integers $(x, x + 1)$ both possible under R_1, there is always a unique value of q, say $q_1(x) = q_1(x, x + 1; m)$ such that x and x + 1 yield the same minimum value in (4); this value of q separates the interval for x from the interval for x + 1. (This property was observed from $m \leq n \leq 16$ and is treated as a conjecture for all m and n in Section 8.)

According to Remark 4 in Section 3 the procedure R_1 for m > 1 is to "break down" the defective set. This "breaking down" is continued until a single unit is established to be defective and removed. It will be convenient to assume, without affecting the properties of the procedure R_1, that the order is randomized only once at the outset.[1] Units or groups of units removed later will then be taken in that order. If the ith unit in that order is the first defective unit, then the "breaking down" mentioned above leads to an H-situation with n - i binomial units and the converse also holds

---

[1] Even this single randomization can be disregarded in carrying out the procedure R_1 if there is no doubt about the assumption of independent chance variables or if the units are already well mixed in the process of delivery to the experimenter.

true.[1] It is convenient to introduce $F_1(m, q) = F_1(m)$ defined as the expected number of group-tests required to "break down" a defective set of size m and for the first time reach an H-situation when q is given. Then $F_1(m)$ clearly does not depend on n and the above argument permits us to write

$$(9) \qquad G_1(m, n) = F_1(m) + \left(\frac{p}{1 - q^m} \right) \sum_{i=1}^{m} q^{i-1} H_1(n - i).$$

For algebraic simplicity we let

$$(10) \qquad G_1^*(m, n) = \left(\frac{1 - q^m}{1 - q} \right) G_1(m, n) \text{ and } F_1^*(m) = \left(\frac{1 - q^m}{1 - q} \right) F_1(m).$$

Then (4) and (9) take on the simpler forms

$$(11) \qquad G_1^*(m, n) = \sum_{i=1}^{m} q^{i-1} + \min_{1 \le x \le m-1} \left\{ q^x G_1^*(m - x, n - x) + G_1^*(x, n) \right\}$$

$$(12) \qquad G_1^*(m, n) = F_1^*(m) + \sum_{i=1}^{m} q^{i-1} H_1(n - i).$$

Substituting (12) in (11), the three summations cancel and the result is

$$(13) \qquad F_1^*(m) = \sum_{i=1}^{m} q^{i-1} + \min_{1 \le x \le m-1} \left\{ q^x F_1^*(m - x) + F_1^*(x) \right\}$$

which does not depend on n. The boundary condition, $F_1^*(1) = 0$ for all q, also does not depend on n. It is clear from this derivation that (13) which does not depend on n, must define the same integer values $x = x_1(q, m)$ as (11) or (4). This proves the following theorem.

Theorem: For any G-situation and any q the size of the next test group, defined implicitly by (4), does not depend on n.

This result simplifies the explicit instructions needed to describe the procedure. Thus the two diagrams, Figures 3 and 4 of [4], describe the procedure R_1 for all values of q and for any $N \le 16$.

Equations (9) and (10) can also be substituted in (3) yielding

$$(14) \quad H_1(n) = 1 + \min_{1 \le x \le n} \left\{ q^x H_1(n - x) + (1 - q) \left[F_1^*(x) + \sum_{i=1}^{x} q^{i-1} H_1(n - i) \right] \right\}$$

---

[1] It follows from the above that for any procedure which "breaks down" the defective set in the above manner (including the method of testing units from the defective set one at a time until a defective unit is found) the expected number of good units eliminated between a G(m, n)-situation and the next H-situation is $q/p - mq^m/(1 - q^m)$ and the number of defective units eliminated is always exactly one.

which together with (13) gives a pair of "one-dimensional" recursion formulas for defining R_1 instead of the "two-dimensional" set, (3) and (4).

Remark 5: If one were to ask for a procedure that "breaks down" the defective set in as small an expected number of group tests as possible then one would write (13) as one of the basic recursion formulas defining the procedure. This shows that R_1 "breaks down" the defective set and returns to an H-situation in a minimal number of tests.

6. The Case $N = \infty$.

In this case the model states that the binomial set remains infinite throughout experimentation but the defective sets and sample sizes will always be finite. Instead of assuming that all units have to be classified as in the case of finite N, we shall now restrict our attention to procedures with the property that the total number of units in all unclassified sets, known to contain any defective units, cannot become indefinitely large. For example, a procedure that always disregards defective sets and continues to take the next test group from the infinite binomial set is eliminated from our present discussion. It will be assumed that the population is denumerably infinite and that the population has been arranged in an ordered sequence $(u_1, u_2, \dots)$. Some procedures, including those proposed below, have the stronger property that u_j is never classified later than u_{j+1} $(j = 1, 2, \dots)$; this can be referred to as the "first come, first served" property. The criterion which seems most appealing for comparing procedures when $N = \infty$ is to consider the limit

$$(15) \qquad C'(q;R) = \lim_{T \to \infty} E \left\{ \frac{\text{Number of units classified in T tests}}{T} \mid R \right\}$$

and one procedure R' is then considered to be better than another R'' over some range of q-values (which we take to be the open interval from 0 to 1) if $C'(q;R') \geq C'(q;R'')$ for all q, with strict inequality for at least one value of q. An optimum procedure is one which maximizes (15) for all q, subject to the above mentioned restriction that the total number of units in all unclassified sets, known to contain any defective units, cannot become indefinitely large. We restrict our attention to values of $C'(q;R)$ on the open interval $0 < q < 1$, and to procedures R for which the right-hand member of (15) is greater than ϵ for some positive ϵ and all q.

It can be shown (at least for the procedures proposed below) that $C'(q;R)$ is the

137

reciprocal of

$$(16) \qquad C(q;R) = \lim_{n \to \infty} E \left\{ \frac{\text{Number of tests to classify n units}}{n} \mid R \right\}$$

(in which the binomial set always remains infinite), and also that

$$(17) \qquad C(q;R) = \lim_{N \to \infty} \left(\frac{H(N)}{N} \mid R(N) \right)$$

where the right-hand member of (17) deals with a finite population of size N, and R(N) is a natural modification of R for finite populations. In fact, R and R(N) can differ only in the H-situation; thus, if R calls for x units, then R(N) will use the smaller of x and the number of "binomial units" remaining. The proof that $C'(q;R)$ is the reciprocal of $C(q;R)$ depends on the fact that the expressions in braces in (15) and (16) can be written as the ratio of means with independent, bounded, and identically distributed summands. Since both means converge with probability 1, we can drop the expectation sign in (15) and (16) without altering the value. Furthermore, the value of $C'(q;R)$ is given by the ratio of expectations

$$(18) \qquad C'(q;R) = \frac{E \left\{ \begin{array}{c} \text{Number of units classified between successive} \\ \text{H-situations} \mid R \end{array} \right\}}{E \left\{ \begin{array}{c} \text{Number of group-tests between successive H-} \\ \text{situations} \mid R \end{array} \right\}}$$

and $C(q;R)$ is the reciprocal of this. The proofs of these results will be published separately.

It follows from the above that if a procedure is asymptotically optimal (i.e., optimal for very large N) in the sense that it maximizes (15) for all q then it is also asymptotically optimal in the sense that it minimizes (16) for all q and vice versa.

A natural modification of R_1 for the case $N = \infty$ will now be defined. In any G-situation, the rule R_1 can be used without change since it was shown above that the size of the next group test depended only on the size of the defective set. In any H-situation, the discussion in [4] is used as the basis of a conjecture that $x_H(q;R_1) \to x_H(q;R_2)$ for any q as $N \to \infty$. The procedure R_2 is defined in Section 15. Since $x_H(q;R_2)$ does not depend on N (assuming N is large), it is natural to use this value for the case $N = \infty$. Let us denote this procedure by R_{21}, since it uses R_2 in the H-situation and R_1 in the G-situation. Of course, R_2 can also be used for $N = \infty$ in both G- and H-situations and we denote this procedure by R_{22}, to make the notation consistent. Finally, two more procedures R_{01} and R_{04} can be defined as follows. In the G-situation

138

we use R_1 and R_4, respectively. For the H-situation we compute the reciprocal of (18) for any arbitrary integer x and then define $x_H(q, R_{0j})$ $(j = 1, 4)$ to be that integer which minimizes the resulting expression, i.e., $x_H(q, R_{0j})$ is the integer for which the minimum

$$(19) \qquad W(q; R_{0j}) = \min_{x = 1, 2, \ldots} \left\{ \frac{p \ [1 + p F_j^*(x;q)]}{1 - q^x} \right\} \qquad (j = 1, 4)$$

is attained. The derivation of the right-hand member of (19) is given in [4] .

TABLE I

Values of C(q;R), C'(q;R) and $x_H(q;R)$, Respectively, for Four Procedures at Three Values of q.

q	R_{01}	R_{21}	R_{04}	R_{22}
	.47251	.47251	.47251	.47251
.90	2.116	2.116	2.116	2.116
	x = 7	x = 7	x = 7	x = 7
	.28808	.28808	.28849	.28853
.95	3.471	3.471	3.466	3.466
	x = 14	x = 14	x = 15	x = 14
	.08105	.08105	.08107	.08126
.99	12.338	12.338	12.335	12.306
	x = 69	x = 69	x = 65	x = 69

Some numerical results for these procedures are given in Table I for q = .90, .95 and .99. One interesting result is that R_{21} appears to be identical with R_{01}. The author has proved this equivalence in general under the assumption that, for R_{01}, the right member of (19) has a unique minimum (or that the integer x at which the minimum in (19) is attained is such that $F_1^*(x;q)$ is given by (23) below); but the assumption of a unique minimum has not been proved and hence the general result must be regarded as a conjecture. In view of the remark in Section 5 that in a G-situation the procedure R_1 returns to an H-situation in a minimal expected number of tests, we have some grounds for conjecturing that R_{21} is an optimal procedure in the sense of (15) or (16) for the case $N = \infty$, among the class of procedures for which the total number of units in all unclassified sets known to contain any defectives remains

139

bounded. For values of q close to unity, the results for R_{04} are very close to the results for R_{21} (or R_{01}) but the values of $x_H(q, R_{04})$ have not yet been computed for as many values of q as have the values $x_H(q, R_{21})$. Furthermore, the procedure R_{04} does not possess the property (that R_4 possesses) that it can be carried out without knowing the true value of q.

Application: In some problems, units come off an assembly line (or a conveyor belt) and the size of the population is conceptually infinite, although the number of units available may actually be quite small at any given time. The rate at which units become available is assumed to be matched to the average rate of testing, so that the experimenter always has enough units to carry out any particular procedure. If every unit that comes off the assembly line has to be classified and the number of such units is not known at the outset, then the infinite model, i.e., the model with $N = \infty$, is appropriate.

7. Properties of R_1 for q Close to Unity.

Returning to the case of a finite population size, it is shown in [4] that for a $G(m, n)$-situation with q in an interval ending at unity (i.e., $q(m) < q < 1$), the size $x = x_G(m; q, R_1)$ of the next group test is such that, depending on m, either x is a power of 2 or m - x is a power of 2. A more precise statement of this result requires some definitions. Let $x_{max} = x_{max}(m; q)$ denote the largest value of x assigned by R_1 in a $G(m, n)$-situation as q varies in the open interval, $0 < q < 1$. It has been numerically shown for $m \le n \le 16$ (and is conjectured for all m, n) that, under R_1, the integer x_{max} occurs in an interval of q-values ending at unity. For $m \ge 2$, let the integers $\alpha(m)$, $\beta(m)$ be defined by

(20) $\qquad m = 2^{\alpha(m)} + \beta(m) \qquad\qquad (0 \le \beta(m) < 2^{\alpha(m)})$,

which is consistent with (8). Then the above-mentioned result states that, under R_1, in any $G(m, n)$-situation, there is an interval of q-values ending at unity in which the value of x is given by

(21) $\qquad x = x_{max} = \begin{cases} 2^{\alpha(m)-1} & \text{for } m \le 3 \cdot 2^{\alpha(m)-1} \\ m - 2^{\alpha(m)} & \text{for } m \ge 3 \cdot 2^{\alpha(m)-1}. \end{cases}$

As a corollary, it follows that for any $G(m, n)$-situation, under R_1,

(22) $\qquad m/3 \le x_{max} \le m/2$.

Also, in the above-mentioned interval, ending at unity,

140

$$(23) \qquad F_1^*(m) = \alpha(m) \left(\frac{1 - q^m}{1 - q} \right) + q^{m - 2\beta(m)} \left(\frac{1 - q^{2\beta(m)}}{1 - q} \right)$$

$$(24) \qquad H_1(n) = q + np + pF_1^*(n) + p^2 \sum_{j=2}^{n-1} F_1^*(j)$$

and expressions for $G_1^*(m, n)$ in terms of $F_1^*(j)$ for $j \leq n$ are given in [4]. If we let q approach unity in these results then we obtain

$$(25) \qquad \lim H_1(n) = 1$$

$$(26) \qquad \lim F_1^*(m) = m\alpha(m) + 2\beta(m)$$

$$(27) \qquad \lim G_1^*(m, n) = \begin{cases} m[1 + \alpha(m)] + 2\beta(m) & \text{for } n > m \\ m[1 + \alpha(m)] + 2\beta(m) - 1 & \text{for } n = m. \end{cases}$$

If the sign of the slope of these functions (at least for q close to unity) can be determined then the above expressions furnish rough bounds for large value of q. For example, it is easy to show that $F_1^*(m)$ is continuous and strictly increasing for all q so that (26) furnishes an upper bound for all q.

8. Conjectured Properties of R_1.

In this section we state some properties which appear to hold for Procedure R_1, based on numerical calculations for $N \leq 16$, but which have not been proved for all N.

A. For any G-situation with fixed $m > 1$, if $x_G(m;q)$ denotes the size of the next test group under R_1 then $x_G(m;q)$ is a non-decreasing step function of q with step size unity, i.e., for any $q \leq q + \epsilon \leq 1$, $\epsilon > 0$,

$$(28) \qquad x_G(m;q) \leq x_G(m;q + \epsilon)$$

and for sufficiently small ϵ

$$(29) \qquad x_G(m;q + \epsilon) \leq x_G(m;q) + 1.$$

Also for fixed q the value of $x_G(m + 1;q)$ is either the same or one greater than $x_G(m;q)$, i.e.,

$$(30) \qquad x_G(m;q) \leq x_G(m + 1;q) \leq x_G(m;q) + 1.$$

The assumption used in Section 7 that the largest x-values are associated with the largest q-values is a simple consequence of (28).

B. For any H-situation we can define $x_H(n;q)$ similar to $x_G(m;q)$ and the property corresponding to (28) still holds; namely that for $q \leq q + \epsilon \leq 1$ and all positive integers n

$$(31) \qquad x_H(n;q) \leq x_H(n;q + \epsilon).$$

It is clear from the tabulations in [4] that the analogs of (29) and (30) do not hold for

141

$x_H(n;q)$.

C. Assume it to be given as part of the problem that it is impossible or economically impractical to identify or keep separate the individual units within any set formed in the course of carrying out procedure R_1. Then the past history of individual units is lost and it can be assumed that, after each test on a batch of x units, the disposition of the x units is made on a batch basis. In this problem it is conjectured that the procedure R_1 is the optimal procedure for all values of q.

9. Properties of R_1 for q Close to Zero.

The procedure R_1 has the interesting property that, for $q < q_0 = (1/2)(\sqrt{5}-1) \doteq .618$, for all integers m, n($2 \leq m \leq n$), the units are all tested one at a time. This same property was recently shown by Ungar [6] to hold for the optimal procedure for any N (without specifying what the optimal procedure is like for any $q > q_0$). The same property also holds for the "information" procedure R_2, for the procedure R_3 defined in [4] , and for the "mixing" procedure R_0 defined in Section 13 below. It also holds for several generalizations discussed in Section 11.

A formal statement of the above result for R_1 will now be stated as a theorem.

Theorem 2: Under procedure R_1 with $2 \leq m \leq n$ and $0 \leq q < q_0$

(32) $\qquad x_G(m;q) = x_H(n;q) = 1$

(33) $\qquad H_1(n) = n$

(34) $\qquad G_1(m, n) = n - \dfrac{pq^{m-1}}{1-q^m}$

(35) $\qquad F_1(m) = \dfrac{1}{p} - \dfrac{[pq^{m-1} + mq^m]}{1-q^m}.$

The proof is given in Section VIII of [4] .

10. A Suggested Procedure for the Case of Unknown q.

It is reasonable to expect that a knowledge of good procedures for the case of known q will suggest good procedures for the case of unknown q. From this point of view we consider modifications of the basic procedure R_1 which make it adaptable when q is unknown. It is suggested that after each test we form a new estimate of q and that the procedure R_1 be used with the estimated value in place of the true value. At the outset we can start with an estimate based on past experience or we can start by testing one unit at a time. A thorough investigation of the relative merit of this procedure has

142

not been carried out. Some discussion on the maximum likelihood method of estimating q is given below.

Let d and s denote the number of units proven defective and proven good, respectively, so that at any stage of experimentation we have

(36) $\qquad N = d + s + m + (n - m) = d + s + n.$

The likelihood L of the observed result (36) is given by

(37) $\qquad L = \binom{N-n}{d} \; p^d \, q^{N-n-d} (1 - q^m).$

Then it is easily shown that

(38) $\qquad \frac{d}{dq} (\log L) = - \frac{d}{dp} (\log L) = - \frac{1}{pq} \left\{ d - (N-n)p + \frac{mpq^m}{1 - q^m} \right\} \; .$

Setting the latter equal to zero, we find that for $m \geq 2$ the maximum likelihood estimate $\hat{q}$ of q is a real positive root of the mth degree polynomial

(39) $\qquad s = d \sum_{i=1}^{m} \hat{q}^i + (m + s) \hat{q}^m$

and for m = 0 we have $\hat{q} = s/(d+s)$, the usual estimate. For s = 0 and $m + d \geq 1$ we get $\hat{q} = 0$ and for $s \geq 1$ it is easily seen, using Descartes "Rule of Signs," that (39) has exactly one real positive root $\hat{q}$ which must lie in the unit interval and hence $\hat{q}$ is uniquely defined. The remaining case s = m = d = 0 can only occur at the outset when there is no observation on which to base an estimate. It is interesting to note that the same result (39) can also be obtained by computing the conditional expected proportion of defectives among the N units given the observed s, d, m, and n and set it equal to $1 - \hat{q}$. The equation thus obtained is the same as (39) and its root is $\hat{q}$.

It may be desirable to test several units one at a time at the outset until a stable estimate of q can be obtained. If the first estimate of q is based on past experience then it is desirable that past experience together with the past observations should enter into the second, third and other early estimates of q. Otherwise, we may obtain sudden jumps from small test groups to large test groups and vice versa, both of which are undesirable.

The above method of getting an estimate is being suggested in connection with procedure R_1 but it can also be used in connection with procedure R_2 without any change. For procedure R_3 of [4] we can have several defective sets and several binomials at

143

any one time and a generalization of (39) is given in [4] for this case. A discussion of the asymptotic variance is also given in Section IX of [4].

11. Some Generalizations of R_1.

Returning to the case of known probabilities q, we now mention some different generalizations of the same basic problem. The same method of deriving a recursion formula with boundary conditions is applicable to most of these problems and, in some cases, the details can be found in Section XI of [4].

1. Two (or more) different kinds of units with known probabilities (say, $q_1 \leqq q_2$) of a good unit are present and both can be put into the same test group. In this case it turns out that units are tested one at a time in both G- and H-situations if

$$1 - q_2 - q_1 q_2 > 0.$$

2. Two (or more) experimenters are working on a single set of N units by carrying out simultaneous, parallel group tests (each of which takes the same fixed time) and cooperating so as to minimize the time required to complete the classification. It is shown in [4], for N = 4 with two experimenters, that with cooperation the expected time can be made smaller than if each experimenter were given two units and told to work independently of each other. This improvement is at the expense of a slight increase in the expected total number of tests.

3. The basic problem is to be carried out under the added restriction that no one unit can be included in more than k group tests. This is particularly appropriate in the blood testing application where a single blood sample can be divided into k equal portions (one for each test) and the patient does not want to be annoyed by having more than one blood sample taken. In this problem it is necessary to work with vectors; for example, $\vec{m} = (m_0, m_1, \ldots, m_{k-1})$ is used to denote the entire defective set and m_j denotes the number of units in $\vec{m}$ that have already been included in j tests (j = 0, 1, ..., k-1). Recursion formulas, with vector arguments, are given in [4]. It appears that, in this case also, units are tested one at a time if $q < q_0 \doteq .618$. The case k = 2 is necessarily based on the method of Dorfman [1], i.e., if a group-test fails then the units therein are all tested individually. The case k = 3 has been numerically computed for small values of N and for all q; this will be published separately.

4. Various generalizations appear if it is assumed that each test on x units gives three (or more) different possible results. For example, a test could indicate that

144

either i) all are good or ii) all are defective or iii) there are at least one good unit and at least one defective present.

5. If a unit can be defective in either of two ways (say, electrical or mechanical) with a priori probabilities of being defective independent but not necessarily equal and if there are two different tests corresponding to the two types of defectives then in addition to deciding the next test group size it may also be necessary to decide which test to use next.

6. For positive continuous chance variables (like weight) the following problem is analogous. A bag of N coins contains good coins of constant weight, say unity, and faulty coins whose weights independently follow a known distribution, which allows all values greater than unity and no values less than unity. Any number of coins can be employed in a single weighing. The problem is to find a procedure for classifying each of the coins in a minimal expected number of weighings, assuming that each coin has known a priori probability q of being good and p = 1 - q of being defective.

Many of these generalizations have not yet been fully investigated.

12. Bounds from Information Theory and Coding Theory.

A lower bound of $H(n)/n = E\{T; q, n, R\}/n$ for any procedure R, which depends on q but not on n, can be readily obtained from information theory. Thus the entropy (or information, measured in bits) associated with the classification of n independent binomially-distributed observations with parameter q (or p = 1 - q) is given by

$$(40) \quad I_H(n; q) = -\sum_{i=0}^{n} \binom{n}{i} p^i q^{n-i} \log_2(p^i q^{n-i}) = -n \left[p \log_2 p + q \log_2 q \right].$$

This entropy must be equal to the expectation (with respect to the chance variable T) of the entropy associated with a succession of T group tests, which always terminates when (and only when) all the units are classified. Since the entropy associated with each test is at most unity, we have for any procedure R and any q

$$(41) \quad H(n) \geq -n \left[p \log_2 p + q \log_2 q \right]$$

and dividing both sides by n gives the desired result. In particular, for procedure R_1, this gives .08079 as a lower bound for $H_1(n)/n$ for all n. It follows from Table II that the difference .08320 - .08079 = .00241 is an upper bound on the difference between $H_1(100)/100$ and the optimal value of $H(n)/n$ attainable under any procedure; furthermore, if $n \to \infty$, this upper bound decreases with n and, by Table I, it approaches

145

.08105 - .08079 = .00026. This shows that the lower bound (41) is not attainable under procedure R_1 for any n, at least for q = .99; it is conjectured that it is not attainable under any group-testing procedure for any q, except q = 1/2. In particular, for q approaching zero or one and fixed n, the lower bound (41) approaches zero while, for the best procedure R, $H(n;R) \to n$ for $q \to 0$ and $H(n;R) \to 1$ for $q \to 1$. Although the lower bound (41) is not generally attainable, it gives a close numerical approximation to $H_1(n)$ for large n, provided that $q \geq 1/2$. The right-hand member of (41) will be referred to as the "Information Lower Bound" or ILB.

As a result of the construction in Section 14 below, it can also be shown for the procedure R_1 that

$$(42) \qquad H_1(n) \leq -n \left[p \log_2 p + q \log_2 q \right] + np$$

so that, using (41), $H_1(n)/n$ differs from the ILB/n by at most p. This is not as strong as the numerical results above for p = .01, but it is simple, general and does not require any computation.

Lower bounds for F(m) and G(m, n), corresponding to (41), which hold for any procedure R and any values of m, n and q, are

$$(43) \qquad F(m) \geq -\sum_{i=1}^{m} \frac{pq^{i-1}}{1-q^m} \log_2 \left(\frac{pq^{i-1}}{1-q^m} \right) = -\log_2 \left(\frac{p}{1-q^m} \right) - \left[\frac{q}{p} - \frac{mq^m}{1-q^m} \right] \log_2 q,$$

$$(44) \qquad G(m, n) \geq -\sum_{i=1}^{m} \frac{pq^{i-1}}{1-q^m} \left[\log_2 \left(\frac{pq^{i-1}}{1-q^m} \right) + (n-i)(p \log_2 p + q \log_2 q) \right]$$

$$= \frac{1}{1-q^m} \left[q^m \log_2 q^m + (1-q^m) \log_2 (1-q^m) \right]$$

$$- \left(n + \frac{mq^m}{1-q^m} \right) (p \log_2 p + q \log_2 q).$$

It is also possible to obtain a better lower bound for each q by the application of a result due to Huffman [3] in coding theory. Starting with n binomial units, we can regard them as ordered. Since each unit is good or defective, there are 2^n possible states of nature, one of which is true. If we represent each test that succeeds by the digit 'zero' and each test that fails by the digit 'one,' then a procedure (for any fixed q) is identical with a binary code. Moreover, a particular set of test outcomes (or a particular stopping point) corresponds in a one-to-one manner with a particular "word" of the code. (In all procedures of interest, the number of stopping points is

146

exactly 2^n, one for each state of nature.) Then the expected number of tests required is identical with the expected word length (i.e., the cost) of the code. Huffman [3] gives a routine for finding the code with the smallest cost. Starting with 2^n states of nature with known probabilities, which for our problem are $(q^n, pq^{n-1}, pq^{n-1}, \ldots, p^n)$, we can construct the optimal code or at least find its cost. This optimal code may or may not correspond to a group-testing procedure but its cost will be a lower bound to the expected number of tests required for any group-testing procedure. Unfortunately, there is no simple analytic expression known to the author for this cost, only a routine for its computation, which is very time-consuming to compute for large n even on modern electronic calculators. Some numerical values of this lower bound (which we denote by HB) are given in Table II for q = .90, .95, .99 and small values of n.

To explain the computation, let $Q_i (i = 1, 2, \ldots, I = 2^n)$ denote any set of a priori probabilities that sum to unity. Order the Q_i, add the two smallest, reorder the remaining set of I - 1 probabilities, add the two smallest, reorder the remaining set of I - 2 probabilities, etc. Let S_j denote the sum of the two smallest probabilities at the jth step (j = 1, 2, \ldots, I - 1), so that $S_{I-1} = 1$. Then the Huffman lower bound (HB), which depends on q and n, is given by

$$(45) \qquad HB = \sum_{i=1}^{I-1} S_i.$$

In every case, this appears to be a greater lower bound than the ILB; Table II shows that the improvement is best for values of q very close to unity.

13. On the Lack of Optimality of R_1.

In [4] it is shown that for q close to unity, starting with a finite binomial set, it is possible to define procedures that are better than R_1. Such procedures will necessarily involve "mixing", i.e., at least one group test is performed on a mixed set of units, some of which are taken from a binomial set and the rest from a defective set, with neither subset empty. A particular procedure R_0, which allows a limited amount of mixing, will now be defined. No mixing procedure has been found which is better than R_0 even for a single value of q. It is known that R_0 is optimal for very small values of n (like n = 2, 3 and 4) but it is not known whether or to what extent it continues to be optimal for intermediate and large values of n. Some numerical results for R_0 are given in Table II, in comparison with the results for R_1 and the lower

147

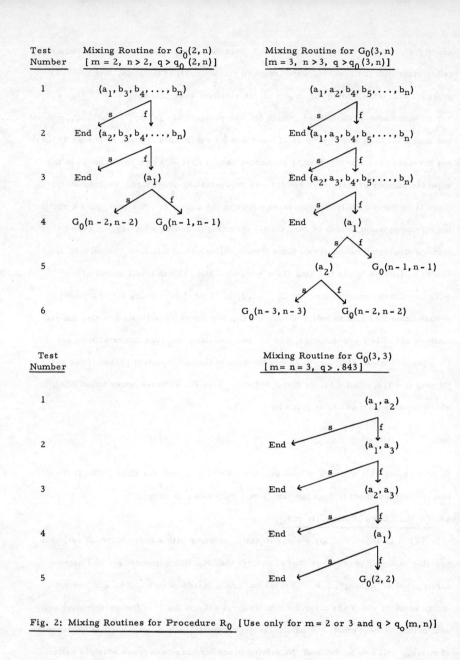

Fig. 2: Mixing Routines for Procedure R_0 [Use only for m = 2 or 3 and q > q_o(m,n)]

bounds discussed in Section 12.

Procedure R_0: Mixing is allowed only when the size of the defective set m is two or three. Three cases are considered according as $n > m = 2$, $n > m = 3$ or $n = m = 3$; the case $n = m = 2$ and all other cases with $m > 3$ are treated in a manner similar to that of R_1, without mixing. In each of the three cases, we define a short "routine", at the end of which (if the test hasn't already terminated) the a posteriori distribution is exactly the same as in a $G(m, n)$-situation with $m = n$. Let $a_1, a_2, \ldots, a_m$ denote the defective set and let $b_{m+1}, b_{m+2}, \ldots, b_n$ denote the binomial set at some stage of experimentation just before the mixing routine is applied. The three diagrams (or trees) in Figure 2 will explain in detail the three mixing routines, which are used only for q sufficiently large, i.e. for $q > q_0(m, n)$. In each case the value of $q_0(m, n)$ is never less than .843.

Let $G_0''(m, n)$ denote the expected number of (additional) group-tests required to terminate experimentation if we start at the beginning of one of the above mixing routines. Then for the three cases $n > m = 2$, $n > m = 3$, $n = m = 3$, respectively, assuming in each case that $G_0(m, n)$ has already been defined for smaller values of n, we obtain

$$(46) \qquad G_0''(2, n) = \frac{3pq^{n-1}}{1-q^2} + \frac{pq(1-q^{n-2})}{1-q^2} \left[3 + G_0(n-2, n-2)\right]$$

$$+ \frac{p(1-q^{n-1})}{1-q^2} \left[3 + G_0(n-1, n-1)\right]$$

$$(47) \qquad G_0''(3, n) = \frac{6pq^{n-1}}{1-q^3} + \frac{pq^2(1-q^{n-3})}{1-q^3} \left[5 + G_0(n-3, n-3)\right]$$

$$+ \frac{pq(1-q^{n-2})}{1-q^3} \left[5 + G_0(n-2, n-2)\right] + \frac{p(1-q^{n-1})}{1-q^3} \left[4 + G_0(n-1, n-1)\right]$$

$$(48) \qquad G_0''(3, 3) = \frac{6pq^2}{1-q^3} + \frac{4p^2q}{1-q^3} + \frac{p(1-q^2)}{1-q^3} \left[4 + G_0(2, 2)\right] = \frac{3(2+q-q^2)}{1+q+q^2} \quad .$$

Let $G_0'(m, n)$ for $n \geq m \geq 2$ be defined (without mixing on the next step but possibly with mixing on subsequent steps) by

$$(49) \qquad G_0'(m, n) = 1 + \min_{1 \leq x \leq m-1} \left\{ \left(\frac{q^x - q^m}{1 - q^m}\right) G_0(m-x, n-x) + \left(\frac{1 - q^x}{1 - q^m}\right) G_0(x, n) \right\},$$

assuming $G_0(m, n)$ has already been defined for smaller n values and also if the n values are the same, for smaller m values. The recursion formulas, which define the

149

procedure R_0, are given for all q in terms of (46), (47), (48) and (49) by

(50) $\qquad H_0(n) = 1 + \min_{1 \leq x \leq n} \left\{ q^x H_0(n-x) + (1-q^x) G_0(x, n) \right\}$ for $n \geq 1$

(51) $\qquad G_0(m, n) = G_0'(m, n)$ $\qquad\qquad\qquad\qquad$ for $n \geq m \geq 4$

(52) $\qquad G_0(m, n) = \min \left\{ G_0'(m, n), G_0''(m, n) \right\}$ $\qquad$ for $n > m = 2$, $n > m = 3$

$\qquad\qquad\qquad\qquad\qquad\qquad\qquad\qquad\qquad\qquad\qquad\qquad\qquad$ and $n = m = 3$

(53) $\qquad G_0(2, 2) = \dfrac{2+q}{1+q}$

The boundary conditions are the same as for R_1, namely

(54) $\qquad H_0(0) = 0$ and $G_0(1, n) = H_0(n-1)$ $(n = 1, 2, \ldots)$.

The problem of giving instructions for carrying out R_0 is more complicated since for any $G_0(m, n)$-situation with values of q close to unity the size of the next test group depends on both m and n. In particular, if $q_0(2, n)$ and $q_0(3, n)$ denote the left end points of the interval where the appropriate mixing routine is applied for m = 2 and 3, respectively, then it is clear from the computations that these points vary with n. In fact, the computations show that these points are non-decreasing functions of n and approach unity for both m = 2 and m = 3. In other words, for any fixed q, the procedure R_0 appears to disregard mixing for all $n > n_0(q)$.

Instructions for carrying out the procedure R_0 are given in Figure 3 for all q for m = 1(1)n and n = 1(1)8. The sum of two numbers (say, $d_0 + b_0$) in Figure 3 indicates that the appropriate mixing routine is to be performed, by mixing d_0 units from the defective set with b_0 units from the binomial set, for the next test.

It will be useful to give an explanation (not a rigorous proof) of why mixing routines are introduced for m = 2 and 3 and not for $m \geq 4$. For q asymptotically close to unity $(q \cong 1)$, it can be assumed that a defective set has exactly one defective unit and that a binomial set probably has no defective units. Let $G(m, n \mid q \cong 1)$ denote the limit of $G(m, n)$ as q tends to unity for any procedure. For any fixed n with m = 2 < n or $m = 3 \leq n$, we wish to prove that $G_0''(m, n \mid q \cong 1)$ is smaller than $G_0'(m, n \mid q \cong 1)$, thus showing that mixing is preferable for large q. For m = 2 < n, we obtain

(55) $\qquad G_0''(2, n \mid q \cong 1) = (1/2)1 + (1/2)2 = 3/2 < 2 = G_0'(2, n \mid q \cong 1)$.

For $m = 3 \leq n$, we obtain for the mixing routine described above

(56) $\qquad G_0''(3, n \mid q \cong 1) = 2 < 7/3 = (1/3)2 + (2/3)(1 + 3/2) = G_0'(3, n \mid q \cong 1)$,

using the first member of (55) to compute the last member of (56). For any fixed n with $m = 4 \leq n$, we wish to prove that $G_0''(m, n \mid q \cong 1) \geq G_0'(m, n \mid q \cong 1)$, thus showing

150

that mixing is not necessarily preferable for large q; here it is assumed that $G_0''(m, n)$ is defined for $m \geq 4$ in the best manner similar to the above mixing routines. For $m = 4 \leq n$, we obtain for the best mixing routines

(57) $\qquad G_0''(4, n \mid q \overset{\sim}{=} 1) = 5/2 = G_0'(4, n \mid q \overset{\sim}{=} 1) = G_0(4, n \mid q \overset{\sim}{=} 1),$

using the first member of (55) to compute the last two members of (57). Similarly, for $n \geq m \geq 5$, we find that $G_0''(m, n \mid q \overset{\sim}{=} 1)$, under the best mixing routine, is no better than $G_0'(m, n \mid q \overset{\sim}{=} 1)$ and there is no clear advantage in using any mixing routine.

It is clear from the definition of R_0 that it must be at least as efficient as R_1 for all m, n and q. Equations (55) and (56) show that it is actually better for q sufficiently close to unity. Numerical computation indicates that (if we start with all units in the binomial state) R_0 and R_1 are identical for $0 \leq q \leq (1 + \sqrt{33})/8 \doteq .843$ and that R_0 is better for $.843 < q < 1$, provided $n \geq 3$. In particular, it follows from the above that under R_0 (as for R_1) all units are tested one at a time for $q < q_0 = (\sqrt{5} - 1)/2 \doteq .618$.

It is also interesting to note from the three mixing routines in Fig. 2 that R_0 preserves the "first come, first served" property.

14. An Alternate Method for Carrying Out Procedure R_1.

Since the procedure R_1 has been tabulated only for $n = 2(1)16$ for all q and for $n = 17(1)100$ for $q = .90, .95$ and $.99$, it is desirable to have a method of carrying out the procedure for any q and any n, by an algorithm which does not require recursion formulas, and which therefore permits one to compute x's for a particular q and n, without building an entire table. In this section, such a method will be described without giving the proof that the procedure is equivalent to R_1. The Huffman routine [3] and the identity

(58) $\qquad p + qp + q^2 p + \cdots + q^{n-1} p + q^n = 1$

play a central role in this method. Numerical values for the terms in (58) are used and, beyond that, the only computation required is the ordering of probabilities and the addition of pairs of probabilities. The method will be explained with the use of a particular example, viz., $n = 10$, $q = .90$, but the same method can be used for any pair (n, q).

The first step is to carry out the Huffman routine on the $n + 1 = 11$ probabilities in (58), i.e., the terms are ordered, the two smallest are added, the resulting set of $n = 10$ probabilities is reordered, the two smallest are added, etc. The scheme can

151

FIGURE 3

Diagram Showing the Number of Units to be Taken in any H-situation or any G-situation for n = 1 through 8 and m $\leq$ n under Procedure R_0.

(Those G-situations, which will never arise if we start with an H-situation, are omitted from the diagram.)

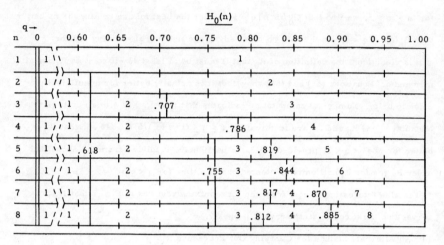

$H_0(n)$

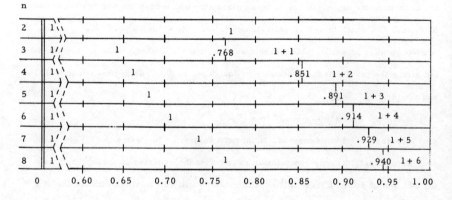

$G_0(m, n)$
m = 2

q = A PRIORI PROBABILITY OF A GOOD UNIT.

152

$$\frac{G_0(m, n) \text{ continued}}{m = 3}$$

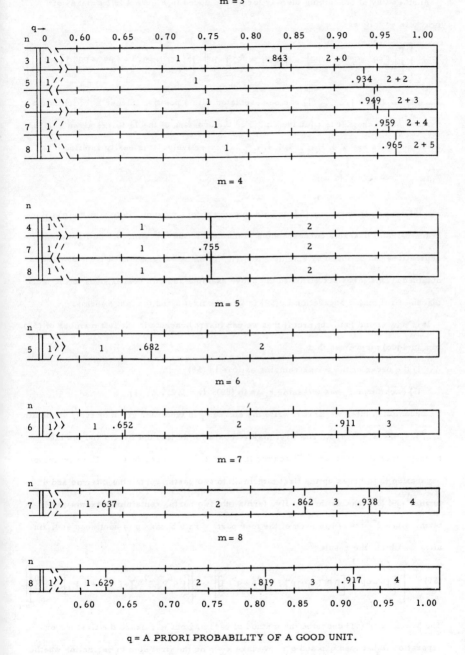

q = A PRIORI PROBABILITY OF A GOOD UNIT.

153

be diagrammed as in Figure 4.

Another way of describing the way terms are added in Figure 4 is by means of brackets as follows

$$(59) \quad \left[\left[\left[\left[pq^9 + pq^8\right] + pq\right] + \left[\left[pq^7 + pq^6\right] + p\right]\right] + \left[\left[\left[pq^5 + pq^4\right] + \left[pq^3 + pq^2\right]\right] + q^{10}\right]\right].$$

Each term T_i $(i = 1, 2, \ldots 11)$ can be associated with a positive integer k_i which is the number of brackets it is contained in. For the ordering of the 11 terms given in (59), these numbers are $4, 4, 3, 4, 4, 3, 4, 4, 4, 4, 2$, respectively. It is easily verified that

$$(60) \quad \sum_{i=1}^{11} 2^{-k_i} = 1$$

and this result is shown in [7] to hold in general for any sum. Note that the position of the pairs of brackets corresponding to the next to the last sum (or the first major separation) can be found by summing the 2^{-k_i} in the order given until the value $1/2$ is obtained. This takes six terms in the above example and this corresponds to the fact that the first major separation in (59) is into the first 6 and the last 5 terms.

It is now stated (without proof) that we can insert brackets in the left member of (58) in a (unique) manner so that

    i) the order of the terms remains as it is in (58)

    ii) each term T_i has the same k_i as in (59) $(i = 1, 2, \ldots, 11)$.

To accomplish this, we first rewrite the eleven k_i in the order given by (58); we obtain $3, 3, 4, 4, 4, 4, 4, 4, 4, 2$. The first major separation is into the first 6 and the last 5 terms, since the first six 2^{-k_i} and the last five 2^{-k_i} each add to $1/2$. The next major separation is to break up the first 6 terms into two parts, containing 2 terms and 4 terms, and to break up the last five terms into two parts, containing 4 terms and 1 term, since $2^{-k_i} = 1/4$ in each of the four parts. This break up is continued and, finally, we obtain the result

$$(61) \quad \left[\left[\left[p + qp\right] + \left[q^2 p + q^3 p\right] + \left[q^4 p + q^5 p\right]\right] + \left[\left[q^6 p + q^7 p\right] + \left[q^8 p + q^9 p\right]\right] + q^{10}\right].$$

The brackets in (61) describe the method of carrying out R_1. Since the first major separation is between $q^5 p$ and $q^6 p$, we take $x = 6$ on the first step to determine whether the first defective is among the first six units or whether the first six are all good.

154

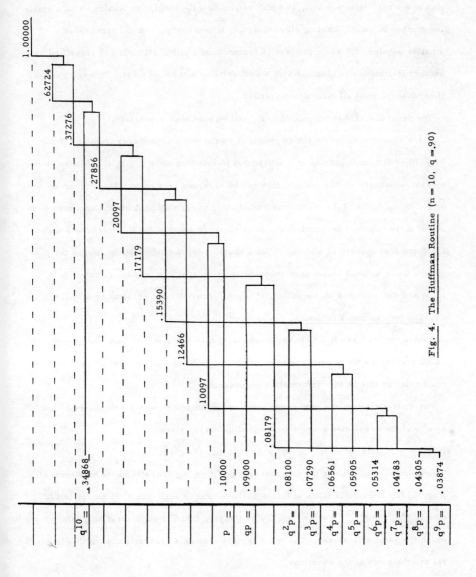

Fig. 4. **The Huffman Routine** (n = 10, q = .90)

If, for example, the first six are good then we proceed to the right in (61) and the next separation is between q^9p and q^{10}; this indicates that we should then test the remaining 4 units. If the first six had at least one failure, then we proceed to the left in (61) and the next separation is between qp and q^2p; this indicates that we should test 2 units from the defective set of size 6, etc.

Either the procedure indicated by (61) leads to termination or it leads to the detection of a single defective unit, at which point a new H-situation is obtained with a smaller number of units. Starting all over again, if necessary, with the same q and a smaller n-value, the same process is repeated until either all units are classified or another H-situation is obtained with a still smaller number of units. This is repeated, if necessary, until all units are classified.

The proof that this is equivalent to R_1 will be published separately.

In the above construction the emphasis is on the way one proceeds from one H-situation either to termination or to a subsequent H-situation after a single defective is removed, whichever comes sooner; this can be regarded as a subproblem. It can be shown on the basis of the above construction that in each subproblem the expected number of tests required to complete the subproblem is equal to the Huffman lower bound, i.e., the cost associated with the Huffman routine for the subproblem. Hence the procedure R_1 is optimal within each subproblem, although, if q is close to unity, N is finite and the units are all identified, it is not optimal for the problem as a whole.

15. The Information Procedure.

Another procedure, R_2, is based on choosing that size x for the next group test which maximizes the entropy (or information) associated with the next group test. We shall refer to this as the "information procedure".

For an H-situation, the next group test has two outcomes with probabilities q^x and $1 - q^x$ and the associated entropy (measured in bits) is given by

$$(62) \qquad I_H(x;q) = - \left[q^x \log_2 q^x + (1 - q^x) \log_2 (1 - q^x) \right].$$

To maximize (62), we use the fact that $(p \log 1/p + q \log 1/q)$ attains its maximum at $p = q = 1/2$. Hence x is taken to be the positive integer such that q^x is closer to $1/2$ than is q^{x-1} or q^{x+1}. For any particular integer, there is an interval of q values for which the same x is chosen. The left and right endpoints, respectively, of this interval are the roots of the equations

(63) $\qquad (1/2)(q^x + q^{x-1}) = 1/2$ and $(1/2)(q^{x+1} + q^x) = 1/2$.

Hence the solution is known if we have a table of dividing points (i.e., q-values) which separate x from x + 1 for each positive integer x; such a table is given in Table VII of [4].

The above is based on the fact that $1 - q^x - q^{x+1}$ has a unique root for every positive integer x and that this root is a strictly increasing function of x. It is interesting to note that the solution above does not depend on the size n of the binomial set.

For a G-situation, the entropy associated with the next group test, based on x units taken only from the defective set, is

$$(64) \qquad I_G(x;q) = - \left[\left(\frac{q^x - q^m}{1 - q^m} \right) \log_2 \left(\frac{q^x - q^m}{1 - q^m} \right) + \left(\frac{1 - q^x}{1 - q^m} \right) \log_2 \left(\frac{1 - q^x}{1 - q^m} \right) \right].$$

To maximize (64), we choose x so that q^x is closer to $(1/2)(1 + q^m)$ than q^{x-1} or q^{x+1}. For a fixed integer x, there is an interval (which may be empty) of q-values for which the same x is chosen; the dividing point between x and x + 1 is the unique root in the interior of the unit interval of

$$(65) \qquad 1 - q^x - q^{x+1} + q^m = 0,$$

whenever (65) has such a root. If the root q = 1 is removed, then (65) becomes

$$(66) \qquad 1 + q + q^2 + \cdots + q^{x-1} - (q^{x+1} + q^{x+2} + \cdots + q^{m-1}) = 0,$$

which clearly has at most one positive root. If the root is not present for some pair (x, m) then x + 1 will never be used for that m under procedure R_2. Since the left member of (65) is a strictly increasing function of x, then for any fixed q with $0 \le q < 1$, $m \ge 2$ and $x \ge (m-1)/2$

$$(67) \qquad 1 - q^x - q^{x+1} + q^m \ge (1 - q^{\frac{m-1}{2}})(1 - q^{\frac{m+1}{2}}) > 0.$$

It follows that the largest x for which the root is present is such that $x + 1 < (m+1)/2$ or $x + 1 \le m/2$ and hence, under procedure R_2, we never take a test group of size greater than m/2. It is interesting to note that the solution in this case depends on m but not on n, as in R_1. Under procedure R_2, the dividing point between x = 1 and x = 2 is the same for each m as under the procedure R_1 (see Table III B of [4]).

Let $F_2(m)$, $F_2^*(m)$, $G_2(m, n)$, $G_2^*(m, n)$ and $H_2(n)$ be defined for procedure R_2 exactly as they were defined for procedure R_1. Then

157

(68) $$F_2^*(m) = \sum_{i=1}^{m} q^{i-1} + q^x F_2^*(m-x) + F_2^*(x) \qquad (m \geq 2)$$

where x is given by the above discussion or by Table VII (G-situation) of [4]. Equations (9) and (12) also hold with all subscripts 'one' replaced by 'two'. Finally,

(69) $$H_2(n) = 1 + q^x H_2(n-x) + p G_2^*(x, n)$$

$$= 1 + q^x H_2(n-x) + p F_2^*(x) + p \sum_{i=1}^{x} q^{i-1} H_2(n-i)$$

where x is given by the above discussion or by Table VII (H-situation) of [4]. The boundary conditions state that $F_2^*(1) = H_2(0) = 0$ for all q. Exact polynomial expressions for $F_2^*(m)$ and $H_2(n)$ are given in Tables VIII and VI, respectively, in [4]. It should be noted that both $F_2^*(m)$ and $H_2(n)$ may have points of discontinuity; at such values of q the polynomial which gives the smaller expectation (and the corresponding x-value) should be used. It should be observed in the numerical comparisons of Table IIIA of [4] that the procedure R_2 compares quite favorably with the procedure R_1 for all values of q. Moreover, the fact that the dividing points are easier to compute makes it easier to apply, since the dividing points for R_1 are known only up to n = 16. It is also interesting to note that the limiting expressions in Table IIIA of [4] as $n \to \infty$ and in Table IIIB of [4] as $m \to \infty$ are the same as the second equation in (63).

It is possible to devise a sequence of procedures $R_2^{(j)}$ such that $R_2^{(1)} = R_2$ and $R_2^{(j)} = R_1$ for j sufficiently large. Under the procedure $R_2^{(j)}$, we choose for the size of the next group test that positive integer x which maximizes the expected information to be obtained from the next j tests in the following sense: it maximizes the ratio of the entropy associated with the next set of (at most) j tests to the expected number of tests, given that the number of tests will not exceed j. For all these procedures, in a G-situation, the next test group is taken only from the defective set.

In the special case when there is no possiblity of stopping before j tests, then we can disregard the denominator (which is a constant j) and simply maximize the information. Since this is always the case for j = 1, then $R_2^{(1)} = R_2$.

Let $M_2^{(j)}(m, n)$ be defined as the maximum number of tests needed in a G(m, n)-situation under procedure $R_2^{(j)}$. Then the associated entropy is independent of x. (It is given by the right-hand members of (41) and (44) in the H- and G-situations, re-

158

spectively.) Hence for $j \geq M_2^{(j)}(m, n)$ the numerator above can be disregarded (i.e., treated as constant) and the problem is to choose that x which minimizes the denominator or the unrestricted expected number of group tests, i.e., $R_2^{(j)} = R_1$ for $j \geq M_2^{(j)}(m, n)$. The value of $M_2^{(j)}(m, n)$, for all $j \geq 1$ appears to be the same as $M_1(m, n)$ defined in (7) for procedure R_1, but this has not been rigorously shown. In all these procedures it is the number of tests required when q is close to unity and the units to be tested happen to be all defective.

For any H(n)-situation with $n \geq 4$ and $j \geq 2$, these procedures appear to eliminate the strategy of taking $x = n - 1$. For example, if $n = 4$, $j = 2$ and $q > .618$, then we wish to compare $x = 2$ and $x = 3$. For $j = 1$, the dividing point between $x = 2$ and $x = 3$ is $q = .755$. Since neither $x = 2$ nor $x = 3$ results in termination after one test, we disregard the denominator and compare (for the starting values $x = 2$ and $x = 3$) the maximum entropies associated with the next two group tests. The results show that $x = 2$ is preferable to $x = 3$ for all $q > .618$. The same result holds for all $j \geq 2$. Then we find that for $j = 2$ the dividing point between $x = 2$ and $x = 4$ is .789. For R_1 the corresponding dividing point is .786.

For all j, we state without proof that in both G- and H-situations under procedure $R_2^{(j)}$ the units are all tested one at a time for $q < (1/2)(\sqrt{5} - 1) \doteq .618$.

This sequence of procedures $R_2^{(j)}$ explains why $R_2^{(1)} = R_2$ is not optimal (it takes into account only the very next test) and how its efficiency can be improved by increasing j. The most efficient procedure in this sequence is R_1.

The author wishes to acknowledge that some of the material in Sections 12 and 14 arose from conversations with Professor Warren Hirsch, New York University, and A. Ross Eckler, Bell Telephone Laboratories. Thanks are also due to Miss Dorothy Kriechbaum, Miss Phyllis Groll, and Miss Ann Graziano, Bell Telephone Laboratories, for their help with the computations in this paper.

TABLE II

Comparison of Expected Number of Tests for R_1 and R_0 and Lower Bounds for Any Procedure Starting with a Binomial set of Finite Size, n. (The three entries in each cell correspond to q = .90, .95 and .99, respectively.)

n	$H(n;q,R_1)$	$H(n;q,R_0)$	Huffman Lower Bound $HB(n,q)$	Information Lower Bound $ILB(n,q)$
2	1.290	1.290	1.290	0.938
	1.148	1.148	1.148	0.573
	1.030	1.030	1.030	0.162
3	1.661	1.627	1.598	1.407
	1.340	1.307	1.300	0.859
	1.070	1.060	1.060	0.242
4	2.051	2.019	1.973	1.876
	1.538	1.505	1.469	1.146
	1.110	1.100	1.091	0.323
5	2.490	2.449	2.401	2.345
	1.771	1.714	1.681	1.432
	1.159	1.141	1.131	0.404
6	2.943	2.911	2.825	2.814
	2.009	1.956	1.897	1.718
	1.208	1.183	1.172	0.485
7	3.414	3.381	3.320	3.283
	2.252	2.191	2.126	2.005
	1.258	1.232	1.213	0.566
8	3.904	3.867	3.806	3.752
	2.499	2.439	2.390	2.291
	1.308	1.282	1.257	0.646
10	4.872	4.834	4.767	4.690
	3.039	2.977	2.920	2.864
	1.425	1.384	1.362	0.808
12	5.790	5.755	5.640	5.628
	3.594	3.533	3.449	3.437
	1.543	1.492	1.467	0.969
20	9.572	9.536		9.380
	5.940	5.872	n.c.	5.728
	2.051	1.977		1.616
40	19.024	18.988		18.760
	11.671	11.607	n.c.	11.456
	3.478	3.384		3.232
60	28.475	28.439		28.139
	17.438	17.372	n.c.	17.184
	5.026	4.936		4.847
80	37.925	37.889		37.519
	23.197	23.132	n.c.	22.912
	6.647	6.557		6.463
100	47.375	47.339		46.899
	28.959	28.894	n.c.	28.640
	8.320	8.227		8.079

n.c. entries were not computed.

BIBLIOGRAPHY

[1] Dorfman, Robert, "The Detection of Defective Members of Large Populations", The Annals of Mathematical Statistics, Vol. 14, 1943, pp. 436-440.

[2] Feller, William, An Introduction to Probability Theory and Its Applications, Vol. 1, 1951, p. 189.

[3] Huffman, David A., "A Method for the Construction of Minimum Redundancy Codes," Proc. I.R.E., Vol. 40, Sept. 1952, p. 1098.

[4] Sobel, Milton and Groll, P.A., "Group Testing to Eliminate Efficiently All Defectives in a Binomial Sample", Bell System Tech. Jour., Vol. 38, Sept. 1959.

[5] Sterrett, Andrew, "On the Detection of Defective Members of Large Populations", The Annals of Mathematical Statistics, Vol. 28, No. 4, 1957, pp. 1033-1036.

[6] Ungar, Peter, "The Cut-Off Point for Group Testing", Submitted to Communications on Pure and Applied Mathematics.

[7] Gilbert, E.N. and Moore, E.F., "Variable Length Binary Encodings", Bell System Tech. Jour., Vol. 38, July 1959, p. 933.

161

SOME OPEN PROBLEMS IN THE FOUNDATIONS OF SUBJECTIVE PROBABILITY[1]

Patrick Suppes

Not only am I the only speaker who is a philosopher, but I am probably the only person attending this conference who is a philosopher; thus I should be expected to give you some words of wisdom. But I really do not have any such words to say. More particularly, I do not want to offer any general defense of subjective probability, or the meaning of subjective probability. I do not mean to admit by this that I am unwilling to offer such a defense. It is just that I do not want to rehash an old story. This morning I am going to talk about more limited problems than a general defense of the meaning and possible applications of notions of subjective probability. Secondly, in talking about problems of subjective probability, I will talk about some problems which interest me. I will not maintain that these problems are the most important, or the most interesting to everyone - they are problems which have interested me. Thirdly, I will be talking in the framework, particularly in the first part of the talk, that Savage introduced in his book, Foundations of Statistics.

The kind of model introduced in that book is as follows: there is a set S of states of nature, a set C of consequences, and a set D of decisions or acts which are functions mapping S into C. The decision-maker's problem is to choose from the decisions or acts that are available one which is in some sense optimal. The analysis which Savage's book leads to is the standard MEU behavioral pattern (maximization of expected utility). Savage introduces seven axioms in terms of an ordering relation $\precsim$ on acts or decisions. For example, Axiom 1 asserts that this relation is transitive and connected. By connected I mean we can weakly choose between any two acts. Naturally though, this axiom does not take us very far. The upshot of the six additional axioms is to yield the MEU result; namely, that if the postulates, in terms of this relation on acts, are satisfied, then we can show that in choosing an act from the set available, a

[1] The research on which this expository paper is based has been supported by the Group Psychology Branch of the Office of Naval Research.

162

person is maximizing expected utility. We mean by this that the person has a utility function on the set of consequences and a subjective probability distribution on the set of states, and the expectancy is with respect to this subjective probability distribution on the set of states.

This kind of maximization of expected utility behavior is not a notion which in any sense originates with Savage; it is very old - in fact it goes back to James Bernoulli in the 18th century. Within this kind of framework there are two major classes of problems that I would like to discuss. The first class of problems, in a certain definite sense, is oriented toward normative behavior, i.e., telling a person how he should behave. The second class of problems is oriented toward a descriptive application. To what extent can we use notions of utility and subjective probability to discuss or to analyze the actual behavior of people? Under the normative heading I will be particularly interested in what I will call problems of axiomatizability and definability, and under the second general heading in what I call behavioristic problems. So let me now address myself to problems of axiomatizability and definability. I want to discuss certain axiomatizability problems that we can raise and which seem to be interesting and somewhat difficult to solve. In discussing these axiomatizability problems there will be some notions perhaps not completely familiar. I will try to indicate intuitively the character of the results, even if I do not explicate all the technical details.

1. <u>Constant acts</u>. A problem which arises immediately in the Savage framework is that of the constant functions or constant acts. By a constant act I mean one that yields the same consequence whatever the state of nature. In more formal terms, a constant act is a function in the set D whose value is the same for all arguments; that is, for all states of nature. Savage's analysis requires that D include the set of all constant acts. An earlier unpublished paper of Herman Rubin's, which assumes some quantitative postulates but is concerned with deriving the existence of a Bayesian distribution on the states of nature, also requires such acts. My own set of axioms [1] , analogous to Savage's but more closely related to the approach (1926) of Frank Ramsey to these problems, demands inclusion of the constant acts.

I know of no analysis which does not require these acts, and yet I want to show by analyzing an example of Savage's just how difficult it is to interpret them. Suppose a

163

man is mixing a six-egg omelet and has put five eggs in a bowl, the problem is what to do with the sixth egg. (For some reason he has a suspicion it may be rotten.) For the moment, we will reduce the problem to two acts - Act I, put egg in a separate bowl; Act II, put egg directly in with other five. The states of nature are S_1 - the egg is rotten, S_2 - the egg is fresh. There are two possibilities. If he puts the egg in a separate bowl and the egg is rotten then he can replace it. He does not ruin the omelet. If he puts the egg in with the other five and the egg is rotten, he ruins all six. I will assume it is very difficult to separate out the rotten egg when it is mixed in with five good ones. On the other hand, it is troublesome and time-consuming to put the egg in a separate bowl. If the man strongly believes the egg is fresh, he is very likely to put it directly into the bowl containing the five other eggs. The constant acts now enter in the following way. In order to prove that the axioms of behavior yield an MEU result, it is necessary (but not sufficient in this case) to extend our set of acts to include the constant acts. In particular, we need to have an act which, even if the egg is fresh, leads to a consequence of ruining the omelet. In other words, totally unrealizable acts are required in order to derive the MEU result. We can certainly, introspectively in some general way, understand what these acts mean. We cannot realize them. To my mind, it is a severe weakness of a theory which claims to be behavioristic to have such acts inextricably included in its formal setup; they hark back all too much to the verbalistic tradition which Savage has so admirably criticized. It is, of course, not playing the game to adopt some ad hoc device like that of a random mechanism whose workings do not affect and are unaffected by goings on in the rest of the world. The assumption of such a mechanism is a patent deus ex machina and nullifies one of the primary aims of the Savage kind of analysis; namely, to extend the theory of rational behavior to areas of action where it is unnatural to think in terms of random mechanisms.

2. Theory of pure rationality. The axioms of the various systems of rational behavior which have been proposed by Ramsey, de Finetti, Savage, and others, including myself, may be divided into two classes. In the first class go those which may be thought of as holding anywhere and anytime. These I call pure axioms of rationality. An example of a pure axiom is the postulate that the preference relation on the set of acts is transitive. In the second class belong those which postulate some special struc-

tural property of the environment and possibly of the decision maker. These I call

structural axioms. The main structural axiom in Savage's setup is, roughly speaking,

that the decision-maker can partition the set of states of nature as fine as he pleases

in terms of probability. The result of this axiom is that there must be, in any model

satisfying Savage's axioms an infinity of states of nature, and given any probability ϵ

no matter how small there is a set of states which has a probability no greater than ϵ.

Such a requirement has nothing in itself to do with the concept of pure rationality, that

is, with the concept of making a rational decision. I consider it a structural imposi-

tion, a limitation on the range of applicability of the theory.

Savage's axiom is, of course, not the only kind of structural assumption which can

be made. In my Berkeley Symposium paper, the number of states of nature is arbi-

trary and I depended on a different kind of structural axiom; namely, that between any

two consequences the decision-maker can find another which is equally spaced in uti-

lity between them. This axiom implies that, except in the trivial case of all consequen-

ces being equally prized, there must be an infinity of consequences. In another pa-

per [2] , Donald Davidson and I used the structural assumption that there are only a

finite number of consequences which are equally spaced in utility.

Two things about these structural axioms should be clear. In the first place, al-

though I have used quantitative or semi-quantitative language in formulating them, all

of them may be formulated in terms of very primitive and qualitative concepts. Se-

condly, in all systems of axioms formulated within the Savage kind of framework with

which I am familiar, such axioms are necessary to prove the MEU kind of result. And

now I want to give some relatively fundamental reasons for this necessity.

To begin with it will be desirable to have a more exact definition of the notion of a

pure axiom of rationality. I say that an axiom of behavior is a pure axiom if and only

whenever it is satisfied in a model M it is satisfied in any submodel of M. Consider,

for instance, the axiom that the preference relation $\leqslant$ on the set D of acts is transi-

tive. Any ordered couple $\mathfrak{U} = <A, R>$ is a possible realization of this axiom if A is

a non-empty set and R is a binary relation on A. A possible realization $\mathfrak{U}$ is a model

of the axiom if the relation R is transitive on A. A model $\mathfrak{U}' = <A', R'>$ is a sub-

model of the model $\mathfrak{U}$ if A' is a subset of A and R' is the relation R restricted to the

set A'. It is easily verified that any submodel of a model of the transitivity axiom is also a model of the axiom, and consequently this axiom is pure. It may also easily be shown that the connectivity axiom for the preference relation $\precsim$ is also a pure axiom. Suppose now we consider an axiom which says three things: (i) the preference relation is transitive on the set of acts; (ii) it is also coneected on this set; and (iii) there is one act which is (weakly) preferred to all others, that is, there is an act d_1 such that for all acts d_2, $d_2 \precsim d_1$. Now this axiom is pure if we restrict ourselves to finite models because any finite model having properties (i) and (ii) will also have (iii). However, if we permit infinite models, then the axiom is no longer pure, because an infinite set which has a greatest element with respect to an ordering relation may have infinite subsets which do not have such an element. For example, the set of all rational numbers x such that $0 \leq x \leq 1$ has 1 as its greatest element with respect to the natural ordering $\leq$, but the subset of numbers such that $0 \leq x < 1$ has no such greatest element. This axiom may suggest that structural axioms are always existential in character, but this is not always the case; for instance, the one Davidson and I used [2] is not existential in form.

The question I now pose is this. What are the possibilities of axiomatizing the theory of pure rationality? In the first place, it is reasonable to restrict ourselves to recursive axiomatizations. A recursive axiomatization of a subject may consist of an infinite list of axioms, but there is a mechanical method for deciding whether or not a statement is an axiom. A simple example of a non-recursive axiomatization may be given for arithmetic, namely the single sentence "A statement S of arithmetic is an axiom if and only if it is true." This axiomatization is non-recursive because it follows from fundamental results of Gödel and Tarski that there is no mechanical method for deciding whether or not a sentence of arithmetic is true.

Secondly, I shall restrict consideration to what are called in logic first-order axioms; that is, we shall permit the variables which occur in the axioms to take as values only the elements of the set D of acts. This is a strong restriction, for it prohibits, for example, any Archimedean axiom which uses an integer-valued variable. The reason for this restriction is that I want to discuss some negative results of a metamathematical or logical character. The difficulties of obtaining any general results on problems of axiomatizability when the axioms are not first-order are considerable. Having imposed the restriction of first-order axioms, it will be necessary to

166

consider only finite models, for it is well-known that if a set of first-order axioms has an infinite model it has an infinite number of models of different infinite cardinality. Consequently it is impossible to give for infinite models first-order axioms on the basis of which the existence of numerical utility or subjective probability functions may be established.

Thirdly, for purposes of simplicity it will be desirable to deal with a situation which permits only two states of nature s_1 and s_2 with equal subjective probabilities. Thus $\sigma(s_1) = \sigma(s_2)$, where $\sigma(s_i)$ is the numerical subjective probability of state s_i. And in terms of expected utility we may then write for d_1, d_2 in D: $d_1 \prec d_2$ if and only if

(1) $\sigma(s_1)u(d_1(s_1)) + \sigma(s_2)u(d_1(s_2)) \leq \sigma(s_1)u(d_2(s_1)) + \sigma(s_2)u(d_2(s_2))$,

where u is the numerical utility function of the set C of consequences. Now since $\sigma(s_1) = \sigma(s_2)$, we have equivalent to (1)

(2) $u(d_1(s_1)) + u(d_1(s_2)) \leq u(d_2(s_1)) + u(d_2(s_2))$,

which in turn is equivalent to

(3) $u(d_1(s_1)) - u(d_2(s_1)) \leq u(d_2(s_2)) - u(d_1(s_2))$.

Whence the theory of pure rationality for this situation of two states of nature with equal probability reduces to axiomatizing the quaternary relation R on the set C of consequences such that there is a numerical function u on C with the property that for every x, y, z, and w in C, $x\,y\,R\,z\,w$ if and only if

(4) $u(x) - u(y) \leq u(z) - u(w)$.

The transformation from the relation $\prec$ on D to the relation R on C is made for technical purposes. Several years ago I thought it would not be a difficult matter to axiomatize R in terms of a finite list of first-order sentences so as to satisfy (4). The problem has not only proved difficult, but in fact Dana Scott and I have shown that it cannot be axiomatized by a finite list of first-order axioms none of which is existential in character [3]. Intuitively it seems that existential sentences cannot offer any real help when it is required that the axioms be closed under submodels, but we have been unable to back up this intuition with a formal proof. So even for this simple case, the problem of finite axiomatization is not settled.

It is possible to give a recursive axiomatization of the relation R (for finite models) by enumeration of what are technically called the isomorphism types of R. We start with sets of cardinality one and list the single isomorphism type, and proceed in this

167

way for each finite cardinal n, listing the types in some fixed order. The difficulty, of course, is that this kind of recursive axiomatization is intuitively completely uninformative. This is by no means always the case with recursive axiomatizations of a theory, as the standard axioms for elementary number theory or those for Zermelo set theory adequately testify. The negative proof given by Scott and me [3] depended upon showing that an infinite but recursive list of axioms which permitted "addition" of intervals is in a certain sense necessary, and at one time we thought a reasonably satisfactory recursive axiomatization could be given which used this addition schema and a finite number of additional axioms. Unfortunately Robert McNaughton produced a counterexample to this system of axioms. His counterexample consists of a set of twenty-two elements; it satisfies the addition schema but does not permit a numerical representation of the kind characterized by (4). It seems that the problem of finding a reasonably appealing recursive axiomatization is difficult.

A fortiori these problems of axiomatization are unsolved for models which permit more states of nature.

3. Behavioristic foundations of subjective probability and utility. From a psychological standpoint the most undesirable thing about the MEU result within the Savage kind of framework is its static character. There is no attempt to explain how an organism comes to have subjective degrees of beliefs about possible states of nature, or evaluations of the relative desirability of different possible consequences. There is no theory as to how the environment interacts with the individual.

I have recently derived from the general assumptions of stimulus learning theory a utility for some simple choice situations [4] . I want briefly to describe these results and then to indicate some of the open problems. Stimulus sampling learning theory was first given a quantitative formulation in 1950 by the psychologist W.K. Estes, and has since been developed by a number of investigators. The basic ideas run as follows. The organism is presented with a sequence of trials on each of which he makes a response that is one of several possible choices. In any particular setup it is assumed that there is a set of stimuli from which the organism draws a sample at the beginning of each trial. It is assumed that on each trial each stimulus is conditioned to exactly one response. The probability of making a given response on any trial is postulated to be simply the proportion of sampled stimuli which are conditioned to that response.

Learning takes place by the following mechanism. At the end of a trial a reinforcing event occurs which identifies that one of the possible responses which was correct. The sampled stimuli become conditioned to this response, and the organism begins another trial in a new state of conditioning.

Naturally this account of stimulus sampling theory is a highly simplified one, and yet it should be clear in what sense this theory is dynamic rather than static, and thus provides a theoretical analysis of how the organism is interacting with its environment.

The kind of utility results obtained from this theory thus far are easily sketched. Suppose a person is on each trial presented with one of several pairs of slot machines. That is, on each trial he chooses which of two slot machines to play, but the pairs presented vary from trial to trial. (When there are exactly two slot machines, this is the familiar two-armed bandit problem.) Let there be N slot machines with π_i the probability of payoff of the ith machine (the probability π_i is not known to the person.) Then the following utility function satisfying a requirement like (4) may be derived from stimulus sampling theory:

$$u(i) = \log \frac{1}{\epsilon_i (1 - \pi_i)} \ ,$$

where ϵ_i is the learning parameter associated with the ith machine.

It is still far from clear how this kind of result may be extended to more complicated behavioral situations. Moreover, it is not yet clear how both subjective probability and utility functions may be derived from stimulus sampling theory even for very simple situations. Positive solution of these problems would provide yet another stepping stone toward the construction of a psychologically sophisticated theory of actual inductive behavior.

BIBLIOGRAPHY

[1] Suppes, P., "The Role of Subjective Probability and Utility in Decision-Making," Proc. of the Third Berkeley Symposium on Mathematical Statistics and Probability (1955), pp. 61-73.

[2] Davidson, D., and Suppes, P., "A Finitistic Axiomatization of Subjective Probability and Utility," Econometrica, Vol. 24 (1956), pp. 264-275.

[3] Scott, and Suppes, P., "Foundational Aspects of Theories of Measurement," Journal of Symbolic Logic, Vol. 23 (1958), pp. 113-128.

[4] Suppes, P., "Behavioristic Foundations of Utility," Technical Report No. 23, Institute for Mathematical Studies in the Social Sciences, Applied Mathematics and Statistics Laboratories, Stanford University, Contract NR 171-034, 1959.

Statistical Decision Theory in Engineering

Lionel Weiss

1. **Introduction**. First we make a quick survey of the two broad fields of "classical statistics": estimation and testing a hypothesis. In a problem of estimation, we are supposed to construct an estimate of an unknown parameter by using observations on a random variable. This estimate is either a single number (a point estimate) or a whole interval (a confidence interval). In a problem of testing a hypothesis, we are to decide whether or not the unknown parameter has some stated property (the hypothesis is that the parameter has this property).

One great advantage of statistical decision theory is that it handles both the problem of testing a hypothesis and the problem of estimation as special cases of a much more general problem. The general problem handled by statistical decision theory can be briefly described as follows. We have to choose one decision out of a given set of possible decisions, after observing the jointly distributed random variables $X_1, \ldots, X_m$, whose joint probability distribution is not completely known, but is known to be one of a given set of possible joint distributions. After the decision is chosen, a loss is incurred which depends on the particular decision chosen and on which particular joint distribution is the actual distribution of $X_1, \ldots, X_m$. (In some problems, the loss may also depend on the observed values of $X_1, \ldots, X_m$).

The problem of estimation is a special case of a statistical decision problem, where the possible distributions of $X_1, \ldots, X_m$ are given by the variation of a parameter, and the possible decisions are the possible values of the parameter. Thus, if the decision chosen is denoted by D, and the true value of the parameter is denoted by θ, the loss might be $(D - \theta)^2$, so our loss increases as our estimate gets farther from the true value.

The problem of testing a hypothesis is a special case of a statistical decision problem where the possible distributions are broken into two groups, group I containing those distributions which satisfy the hypothesis, group II containing the distributions which do not satisfy the hypothesis, and there are two possible decisions, one decision being to state that the distribution is in group I (that is, to accept the hypothesis), the other decision being to state that the distribution is in group II (that is, to reject the hypothesis). If the right decision is chosen, the loss is zero, otherwise it is some positive number.

Of course, there are problems of statistical decision theory which are neither problems of estimation nor problems of testing a hypothesis. Thus statistical decision theory offers simultaneously a mathematical generalization and a mathematical unification of classical statistical theory.

However, it would seem that statistical decision theory as it has been described above (which is the usual description) is not directly applicable to problems arising in practice. Let us take a typical problem of estimation first. Suppose that each month a company sells a certain amount of its product, and that the amounts sold in the various months are independent, identically distributed random variables with a normal distribution with unknown mean and variance. The problem is to estimate this unknown mean and variance, using the observations available. Suppose that this is done by the company statistician. Then what happens? It is hard to believe that a company would retain a statistician to compute these estimates just because of idle curiosity. Presumably, these estimates will be used to forecast future sales. Then why not let the statistician estimate future sales directly? Even in an age of specialization, it seems to be going too far to hire one man to construct estimates of parameters and another man to make forecasts using these estimates. The point is that if the statistician is told to forecast future sales, this does not necessarily have to be done by first estimating the separate parameters. We can go farther, and ask why the company wants to forecast future sales? Clearly, to enable it to take the proper physical or financial action indicated by the forecast: for example, to set the production rate at an optimal level. But then why not let the statistician go directly from the observations to the physical action indicated by the observations, instead of breaking the problem into what seem to be artificial pieces?

Let us apply this same discussion to the general problem of statistical decision theory. In statistical decision theory, the loss depends on the decision chosen and on the true distribution. But in many cases this means that when the loss is actually paid,

171

we will learn exactly which distribution is the true one. This is so because we know the decision we chose, and once we know the loss that must be paid we can solve for the true distribution as the one that yields the given loss in combination with the known decision. However, it is difficult to imagine what mechanism would or could make the true distribution known to us, except for certain artificial game situations. It seems, then, that the loss actually incurred cannot really be a function of the true distribution of $X_1, \ldots, X_m$. What, then, will this actually incurred loss depend on? Recall the problem of forecasting future sales discussed above; in general, the actual loss will depend on random variables $Y_1, \ldots, Y_n$ which will be observed after the decision is chosen, where the joint distribution of $X_1, \ldots, X_m$, $Y_1, \ldots, Y_n$ is not completely known, but is known to be one of a given class of distributions. In the company's sales forecasting problem, the X's were the sales observed before the decision was chosen, the Y's are sales that will be observed after the decision is chosen.

We will see that making the loss depend upon random variables which will be ob - served after the decision is chosen, rather than upon the distribution of the random variables on which the decision is based, does not change the mathematical analysis at all, but does put the problem into the form in which it arises in practice.

2. Notation. Now we set up a system of notation for the general statistical decision problem. $X_1, \ldots, X_m$ denote the random variables on which the decision is to be based: the symbol X denotes the vector $X_1, \ldots, X_m$. $Y_1, \ldots, Y_n$ denote the random variables that will be observed after the decision is chosen: the symbol Y denotes the vector $Y_1, \ldots, Y_n$. We assume for simplicity of exposition that X and Y are discrete random variables. The symbol D is an index for the possible decisions: that is, a particular value of D picks out a particular decision. The loss we incur when $X = x$, $Y = y$, and the decision chosen is D is the function $W(y; D; x)$. In many cases, the loss does not depend explicitly on X, and we write it $W(y; D)$. θ is an index for the possible joint distributions of X and Y. That is, a particular value of θ picks out a particular distribution. $f(x, y; \theta)$ denotes $P(X = x$ and $Y = y)$ under the θth distribution in our list.

A decision rule s is defined by nonnegative numbers $s(x; D)$, where $s(x; D)$ is the probability assigned by the decision rule s to choosing the decision D when $X = x$. Thus, when D can take on only L different values, say $1, 2, \ldots, L$, we have

172

$$\sum_{D=1}^{L} s(x; D) = 1 \quad \text{for each x.}$$

For each given decision rule s, the loss that will be incurred when using s is a random variable whose probability distribution depends on the unknown joint distribution $f(x, y; \theta)$. The expected value of the loss that will be incurred when the decision rule s is used and the joint distribution is the θth in our list will be denoted by $r(\theta; s)$. We have

$$r(\theta; s) = \sum_{x} \sum_{D=1}^{L} \sum_{y} W(y; D; x) f(x, y; \theta) s(x; D),$$

assuming a finite number L of possible decisions. If we denote $\sum_{y} W(y; D; x) f(x, y; \theta)$ by $R(\theta; x; D)$, then we have $r(\theta; s) = \sum_{x} \sum_{D=1}^{L} R(\theta; x; D) s(x; D)$, and $R(\theta; x; D)$ is the loss function of the usual formulation of statistical decision theory. But in no practical case would $R(\theta; x; D)$ coincide with the functions usually assumed in standard decision theory.

3. The evaluation of decision rules. Roughly speaking, we consider a decision rule s "good" when $r(\theta; s)$ is "small" for all θ. To be more precise, suppose we are considering two different decision rules, s_1 and s_2, characterized by the decision probabilities $s_1(x; D)$ and $s_2(x; D)$ respectively. Suppose $r(\theta; s_1) \leqslant r(\theta; s_2)$ for all θ, with $r(\theta; s_1) < r(\theta; s_2)$ for at least one value of θ. Then we say that s_1 is a better decision rule than s_2, and we would not use s_2. A decision rule t is called "inadmissible" if there is a decision rule which is better than t according to the definition just given. Any decision rule which is not inadmissible is called "admissible." Whatever decision is finally used should be an admissible decision rule, and therefore a method for finding admissible decision rules is needed.

4. Bayes decision rules. Suppose that there is a finite number h of possible joint distributions of X and Y, so that we may assume that θ ranges over the values $1, \ldots, h$. If $b(1), \ldots, b(h)$ are nonnegative numbers adding to unity, then a decision rule s is called a "Bayes decision rule relative to $b(1), \ldots, b(h)$" if

$$\sum_{\theta=1}^{h} b(\theta) r(\theta; s) \leq \sum_{\theta=1}^{h} b(\theta) r(\theta; t)$$

173

for each and every decision rule t. A decision rule is called simply a "Bayes decision rule" if it is a Bayes decision rule relative to some set of nonnegative numbers adding to unity.

A basic theorem states that any admissible decision rule is a Bayes decision rule. However, some Bayes decision rules are inadmissible. It may then be wondered why we bother to pay attention to Bayes decision rules, when what we really want are only admissible decision rules. The answer is that it is so simple to find the Bayes decision rules that it is a useful step in searching for the admissible decision rules.

If s is a Bayes decision rule relative to $b(1), \ldots, b(h)$, and all h of these numbers are positive, then s must be admissible. For suppose s were not admissible. Then there would be a decision rule t with $r(\theta; t) \leqslant r(\theta; s)$ for all θ, with $r(\theta; t) < r(\theta; s)$ for at least one value of θ, say for $\theta = j$. But then

$$\sum_{\theta=1}^{h} b(\theta)r(\theta; s) - \sum_{\theta=1}^{h} b(\theta)r(\theta; t) = \sum_{\theta=1}^{h} b(\theta)[r(\theta; s) - r(\theta; t)] \geqslant$$

$$b(j)[r(j; s) - r(j; t)] > 0,$$

which contradicts the fact that s is a Bayes decision rule relative to $b(1), \ldots, b(h)$, and proves that s is admissible.

To construct a Bayes decision rule relative to given $b(1), \ldots, b(h)$, we note that

$$\sum_{\theta=1}^{h} b(\theta)r(\theta; s) = \sum_{x} \sum_{D=1}^{L} s(x; D) \left\{ \sum_{\theta=1}^{h} \sum_{y} b(\theta)W(y; D; x)f(x, y; \theta) \right\}.$$

s is to be chosen to minimize this expression. We denote the expression

$$\sum_{\theta=1}^{h} \sum_{y} b(\theta)W(y; D; x)f(x, y; \theta)$$ by $K(D; x)$. Then s is to be chosen to make

$$\sum_{x} \sum_{D=1}^{L} s(x; D)K(D; x)$$ as small as possible. Clearly, for each pair x, D, we set

$s(x; D)$ equal to zero unless $K(D; x) = \min \left\{ K(1; x), \ldots, K(L; x) \right\}$. If for some x, $K(D; x)$ is minimized for more than one value of D, then there is more than one decision rule which is Bayes relative to $b(1), \ldots, b(h)$.

As an illustrative example, suppose a company is faced with the following problem. It can buy a certain machine from supplier A, who charges $100 and unconditionally

174

guarantees that the machine will operate satisfactorily. Or it can buy a similar machine from supplier B for $70. Supplier B does not guarantee the machine he sells, and if it breaks down, the company will have to buy a machine from supplier A for $100. The machine from supplier B has been made by an unknown one of two possible factories, one of which turns out machines 20% of which are defective, the other factory turning out machines 40% of which are defective. Before the company decides, it can observe the operation of two other installed machines known to be from the same factory that produced the machine offered by supplier B. We turn this into a decision problem of the form we have been discussing by introducing the following notation. The random variable X_1 is defined to be equal to 0 if the first installed machine to be observed breaks down, equal to 1 otherwise; X_2 is defined in the same way for the second installed machine to be observed; Y is defined in the same way in terms of the machine offered for sale by supplier B. From the conditions of the problem, X_1, X_2, Y are all independent and identically distributed, the common distribution being one of the two following distributions:

$\theta = 1$	possible values	0	1
	probability	.2	.8

$\theta = 2$	possible values	0	1
	probability	.4	.6

We label the decision to buy from supplier A as the first decision (D= 1), and the decision to buy from supplier B as the second decision (D = 2). Then the loss function, which does not depend on X_1, X_2, is given as follows:

$W(y; 1) = \$100$ for y = 0 or 1,

$W(0; 2) = \$70 + \$100$,

$W(1; 2) = \$70.$

For this problem, it can be verified that any decision rule s with s(0, 0; 1) = 1 and s(1, 1; 1) = 0 is a Bayes decision rule relative to .6, .4. Any such decision rule is admissible.

5. Minimax decision rules. Since in any given problem there are usually infinitely many admissible decision rules, what further principles can be used to pick one particular decision rule from among all the admissible decision rules? We could claim

175

that it is not the statistician's job to pick one particular decision rule, but to find all the admissible decision rules. Then the person who will actually incur the loss should pick one particular decision rule from among the admissible decision rules presented to him by the statistician. However, some general principles for choosing one particular decision rule have been suggested, though none has been universally adopted.

The most familiar such principle is the minimax principle, which we now describe. For any decision rule s, denote $\max_\theta r(\theta; s)$ by $M(s)$. Then the minimax principle states: choose an admissible decision rule s which minimizes $M(s)$. In other words, use a decision rule which has the smallest maximum expected loss. This principle has been criticized for being too conservative.

What computational techniques can be used to actually find a minimax decision rule? Let V denote $\min_s M(s)$, a quantity which will be unknown at the start of our computations. Then we have to find the quantities $s(x; D)$ so that $r(\theta; s) \leq V$ for $\theta = 1, \ldots, h$ and so that V is minimized. This is a problem in which our unknowns are $s(x; D)$ and V. Since $r(\theta; s)$ are linear functions of $s(x; D)$, we have a typical linear programming problem, to which the simplex method, for example, can be applied. Of course this is so only when we are dealing with a finite number of possible decisions and distributions and our random variables are discrete. However, in many cases infinite situations can be satisfactorily approximated by finite situations.

6. Problems involving a sequence of decisions over time. We denote by $Y(j)$ the vector of random variables that will be observed between the jth time at which we must choose a decision and the $(j + 1)^{st}$ time at which we must choose a decision. X denotes, as usual, the vector that will be observed before any decision must be chosen. $D(j)$ denotes the decision made at the jth time. Suppose that a decision must be made at T different times. Then our loss will be denoted by

$$W(X, D(1), Y(1), D(2), Y(2), \ldots, D(T), Y(T)).$$

The most important fact about the construction of Bayes decision rules in this case is that we must first describe how the decision rule chooses $D(T)$, and then we describe how the decision rule chooses $D(T - 1)$, and then how the decision rule chooses $D(T - 2)$, etc. In other words, we must work our way backwards in the construction of

176

Bayes decision rules. For in order to evaluate the goodness of the decision to be made at any given time, we must know how we will proceed in the future (that is, how we will make future decisions).

In choosing decision $D(j)$, we must of course take into account the already known values of $X, D(1), Y(1), D(2), Y(2), \ldots, D(j-1), Y(j-1)$. Thus for the problem of choosing $D(j)$, the quantities $X, D(1), \ldots, Y(j-1)$ play the same role as the quantities $X_1, \ldots, X_m$ did in the simpler problems where there was only one time when a decision had to be made. Furthermore, when we have to choose $D(j)$, we assume that we have already described how we will choose $D(j+1), \ldots, D(T)$. This means that $D(j+1), \ldots, D(T)$ are expressed in terms of $X, D(1), Y(1), \ldots, Y(j-1), D(j), Y(j), Y(j+1), \ldots, Y(T-1)$. Thus, for the problem of choosing $D(j)$, we have eliminated the variables $D(j+1), \ldots, D(T)$ by expressing them in terms of the other variables. But then the problem of choosing $D(j)$ has been turned into a problem of the type discussed above, with the following correspondences. In our present problem, $X, D(1), \ldots, Y(j-1)$ play the role of $X_1, \ldots, X_m$ in the earlier problem; and in our present problem $Y(j), Y(j+1), \ldots, Y(T)$ play the role of $Y_1, \ldots, Y_n$ in our original problem. Then the construction of a Bayes decision rule proceeds exactly as before. Of course, the construction of an overall Bayes decision rule requires T separate applications of the procedure: one for describing how $D(T)$ is to be chosen, then one for describing how $D(T-1)$ is to be chosen, ..., finally one for describing how $D(1)$ is to be chosen.

Now we describe a numerical example. The period of use of a machine is divided into three time periods: Period 1 is from installation to first overhaul; period 2 is from first overhaul to second overhaul; period 3 is from second overhaul to the replacement of the machine. $D(1)$ is the amount spent on the first overhaul, $D(2)$ is the amount spent on the second overhaul. X is defined to be 1 if the machine breaks down during period 1, and 0 if the machine does not break down during period 1. $Y(1)$ and $Y(2)$ are defined in the same way for periods 2 and 3 respectively. X, $Y(1)$ and $Y(2)$ are assumed to be independent random variables, with $P(X=1)=\theta$, $P(Y(1)=1)$ $=\theta/(1+D(1))$, $P(Y(2)=1)=\theta/(1+\frac{1}{2}D(1)+D(2))$. θ is an unknown number between 0 and 1. If the machine breaks down in any period, it costs \$1000 to put it back in use. Thus $W(X, D(1), Y(1), D(2), Y(2))=D(1)+D(2)+1000(X+Y(1)+Y(2))$.

177

ON CHANNELS IN WHICH THE DISTRIBUTION OF ERROR
IS KNOWN ONLY TO THE RECEIVER OR ONLY TO THE SENDER

J. Wolfowitz

In this note we illustrate, by means of a set of simultaneous semi-continuous channels, some of the results described and proved in [1] (especially Section 8). In Section 7 of this latter paper extension of these results to many other channels, including
some with memory, is indicated. The present note, although intentionally brief, requires for its comprehension no prior knowledge of information theory. For this reason it is necessary to begin with a number of definitions. The meaning of any non-ma-
thematical terms which occur in these will either be precisely explained at once or
will soon become readily apparent.

Let the input alphabet consist of the (real) numbers $a_1, \ldots, a_k$. Define a u-sequence
as any sequence of n numbers, each of which is one of $a_1, \ldots, a_k$. By a v-sequence we
shall mean any sequence of n real numbers. The sender sends (or transmits) u-sequen-
ces through the channel. Any u-sequence transmitted may be garbled by channel noise
(error). Let $u_0 = (x_1, \ldots, x_n)$ be any u-sequence sent. The chance received v-sequence
$v(u_0)$ is a sequence of independent chance variables,

$$v(u_0) = (Y_1(u_0), \ldots, Y_n(u_0)),$$

where $Y_i(u_0)-x_i$ has a Gaussian distribution with mean μ and variance σ^2. Let A be
any set of v-sequences. Then

$$P\{v(u_0) \in A \mid \mu, \sigma^2\},$$

the probability that $v(u_0)$ lies in A, is of course a function of μ and σ^2.

Let J_1 and J_2 be bounded subsets of the real line; J_2 is to contain non-negative numbers only.[1] The parameters μ and σ^2 lie, respectively, in J_1 and J_2, and may vary
<u>arbitrarily</u> from one transmitted u-sequence to another. The case where (μ, σ^2) is
known to both sender and receiver falls within the results of [2]. The case where (μ, σ^2)
is known to neither sender nor receiver is treated in [1]. Here we shall discuss the

---

[1] In [1] there was added the unnecessary condition that J_2 should be at a positive distance from zero.

two cases where I) the receiver knows (μ, σ^2) but the sender does not, and II) the sender knows (μ, σ^2) but the receiver does not. We shall call these, respectively, channel I and channel II. As we have already remarked, the results to be stated are implicit in [1].

A code (N, λ) for channel I is a system of sets

$$B(\mu, \sigma^2) = \{(u_1, A_1(\mu, \sigma^2)), \ldots, (u_N, A_N(\mu, \sigma^2))\}$$

for every μ in J_1 and every σ^2 in J_2, with the following properties:

      a) $u_1, \ldots, u_N$ are u-sequences.

      b) $A_i(\mu, \sigma^2)$, $i = 1, \ldots, N, \mu \in J_1$, $\sigma^2 \in J_2$,

are sets of v-sequences.

      c) For every (μ, σ^2) the sets $A_1(\mu, \sigma^2), \ldots, A_N(\mu, \sigma^2)$ are disjoint.

      d) For every (μ, σ^2) we have

$$P\{v(u_i) \in A_i(\mu, \sigma^2) \mid \mu, \sigma^2\} \geq 1 - \lambda, \quad i = 1, \ldots, N$$

The practical use of such a code is as follows: When the sender wants to send the ith word of a dictionary of N words, he sends the u-sequence u_i. When the receiver knows that μ, σ^2 are, respectively, the mean and variance of the error for a particular u-sequence, and the v-sequence received lies in $A_j(\mu, \sigma^2)$, the receiver concludes that the u-sequence u_j has been sent. The probability that any word (u-sequence) sent will be correctly "decoded" (understood) by the receiver is $\geq 1 - \lambda$.

A code (N, λ) for channel II is a system of sets

$$C(\mu, \sigma^2) = \{(u_1(\mu, \sigma^2), A_1), \ldots, (u_N(\mu, \sigma^2), A_N)\}$$

for every μ in J_1 and every σ^2 in J_2, with the following properties:

      a) $u_1(\mu, \sigma^2), \ldots, u_N(\mu, \sigma^2)$ are u-sequences.

      b) $A_1, \ldots, A_N$ are disjoint sets of v-sequences.

      c) For every (μ, σ^2) we have

$$P\{v(u_i(\mu, \sigma^2)) \in A_i \mid \mu, \sigma^2\} \geq 1 - \lambda, \quad i = 1, \ldots, N$$

The practical use of such a code is as follows: When the sender wants to send the ith word of a dictionary of N words and knows that μ, σ^2 are, respectively, the mean and variance of the error for this particular u-sequence, he sends $u_i(\mu, \sigma^2)$. When the receiver receives a v-sequence in A_j he concludes that the jth word has been sent. The probability that any word sent will be correctly decoded by the receiver is $\geq 1 - \lambda$.

The capacity of a channel is a concept fundamental in information theory. As its colloquial name implies, it is a number which measures a certain capability of the channel. For channels I and II the capacities will be implicitly but precisely defined by Theorems 1 and 2 below. These theorems hold for channels I and II and are to be understood as follows: The number C which occurs in both is to be replaced by C_1, the capacity of channel I, when the theorems are applied to channel I, and is to be replaced by C_2, the capacity of channel II, when the theorems are applied to channel II.

Theorem 1. Let $\epsilon > 0$ and λ, $0 < \lambda \leq 1$, be arbitrary. For n sufficiently large there exists a code $(2^{n(C-\epsilon)}, \lambda)$.

Theorem 2. Let $\epsilon > 0$ and λ, $0 \leq \lambda < 1$, be arbitrary. For n sufficiently large there does not exist a code $(2^{n(C+\epsilon)}, \lambda)$.

The capacities are related as follows:

$$0 < C_1 \leq C_2.$$

In general, $C_1 < C_2$. Let $C(\mu, \sigma^2)$ be the capacity defined by Shannon ([3] ; see also, for example, [2]) of the channel where μ, σ^2 are the mean and variance, respectively, of the error for every u-sequence transmitted (and this fact is, of course, known to both sender and receiver). Then obviously

$$C_2 \leq \inf_{\mu, \sigma^2} C(\mu, \sigma^2)$$

where the infimum is taken over all μ in J_1 and all σ^2 in J_2. A general theorem of [1] implies that actually

$$C_2 = \inf_{\mu, \sigma^2} C(\mu, \sigma^2).$$

The value of C_1, also implied by a general theorem of [1] , is less simple to describe. It will be briefly described in the next paragraph in a manner intelligible only to one with some familiarity with information theory. Readers unfamiliar with information theory are invited to omit the next paragraph and are referred to [1] for a precise, and to them intelligible, description of C_1.

Let π be any stochastic input on the input alphabet $a_1, \ldots, a_k$. For given π and (μ, σ^2) let $H(\pi, \mu, \sigma^2)$ be the usual difference between the Shannon entropy of the output and the conditional entropy of the output, given the input. Then

$$C_1 = \sup_{\pi} \inf_{\mu, \sigma^2} H(\pi, \mu, \sigma^2).$$

In this notation

$$C_2 = \inf_{\mu, \sigma^2} \sup_{\pi} H(\pi, \mu, \sigma^2)$$

This makes it clear at once that $C_1 \leq C_2$.

A general theorem of [1] implies the following: C_1 is the capacity of the channel where neither sender nor receiver knows (μ, σ^2) which varies arbitrarily from one u-sequence to another, μ in J_1 and σ^2 in J_2.

The channels I and II were selected for the illustrative purpose of this note, from among the channels which come within the scope of the results of [1], for their importance and simplicity. It is obvious that if either sender or receiver knows μ he can compensate for μ by subtracting it from each letter. Moreover, this can clearly be done whether or not μ lies in J_1. It follows that C_1 and C_2 do not depend on J_1. (It is trivial to verify that neither $C(\mu, \sigma^2)$ nor $H(\pi, \mu, \sigma^2)$ depend on μ.) Why then was J_1 (or indeed μ) introduced at all? The answer is that it was introduced in order to utilize the results of [1] so as to be able to make the statement of the preceding paragraph. Not only is this latter result interesting per se, but taken in conjunction with the results for channel I it shows that knowledge of the distribution of error for any word (u-sequence) by the receiver alone does not increase the capacity. It is also interesting that, even when neither sender nor receiver knows the distribution of error for any word, the capacity does not depend on J_1.

To sum up: As long as μ and σ^2 are restricted to J_1 and J_2, respectively, and the sender does not know (μ, σ^2), the capacity of the channel is the same whether or not the receiver knows (μ, σ^2), and does not depend on J_1. If σ^2 is restricted to J_2 and is unknown to the sender but known to the receiver, and if μ is unrestricted on the real line but known to the receiver, the capacity of the channel is C_1. Finally we note that obviously

$$C_2 = C(0, t)$$

where t is the supremum of the points of J_2.

Theorem 1 is an example of a coding theorem in information theory, and Theorem 2 is the "strong" converse of Theorem 1. In the "weak" converse the conclusion is the same but the hypothesis is strengthened to require that λ be sufficiently small. For an explanation of why the strong converse is a much deeper result than the weak converse see [1] or [2], and for an example of how they are sometimes confused in the literature see [2] .

Results analogous to all those above hold if one of μ , σ^2 is fixed and only the other is allowed to vary. Of course, as we have seen above, the parameter μ has a special position.

BIBLIOGRAPHY

[1] Wolfowitz, J. "Simultaneous Channels," to appear in Archive for Rational Mechanics and Analysis.

[2] Wolfowitz, J. "Strong Converse of the Coding Theorem for Semi-continuous Channels" Illinois Journal of Math., Vol. 3, No. 4, Dec., 1959.

[3] Shannon, C.E. "A Mathematical Theory of Communication," Bell System Tech. Journal, Vol. 27, (1948), pp. 379-423, pp. 623-656.

INDEX

Accounting, 74, 77
Adaptive systems, x, 50
Admissible decision rules,
    173-174
Aggregation, 87-92
Alcohol plant problem, 41
Allocation, resource, 69
Analysis, sequential, 15-26,
    53-61
Anderson, T. W., 54-56, 59-61
Approximation, 2
Archimedian axiom, 166
Artificial intelligence, 13
Axiomatization, 163-168
    recursive, 166-168

Balance, 62, 65, 77
Balanced margin matrix, 66
Bayes rule, 163, 173-177
Bayes theorem, 18
Behavioral situations, 169
Behavioral systems, 62-85
Behavioristic problems, 163
Bellman, R., 38
Binary symmetric channel, 116
Blood testing, 128, 144
Boolean algebra, 76
Borel field, 116
Box-Wilson procedure, 42-47
Brown, George W., 1-14
Brownian motion, 29-31

Capacitors, tests of, 129
Chapman-Kolmogorov equation, 88
Chernoff, H., 15-26
Chess, 3, 11, 13
Closure, 62, 65, 72, 77
Coding, 93-126, 145, 178-182
Computation, x, 1-14

Connectivity, 162, 166
Consistency, 27-33
Continuity, 32
Conventional system time, 62
Criterion, xi, 7
Cryptostates, 83
Cyclic net, 65

Data processing, 1
Davidson, D., 165-166
Decisioning, sequential, 34-52
Definability, 163
Design of experiments, 15-26
Difference distortion measure,
    120
Distortion, 93-126
Donnelly, T. G., 54-55
Doob, J. L., 27-33
Dorfman, R., 144
Duality, 126, 129
Duel, 39
Dyadic relation, 63
Dynamic economic equilibrium,
    67, 80
Dynamic programming, 38

Economic equilibrium, dynamic,
    67, 80
Economics, statistical, 62, 65,
    74, 77, 78
"Entity" (of proper parts), 62, 77,
    79
Entropy, 101, 145, 156, 180
Ergodic process, 105-109, 123
Estes, W. R., 168
Estimation, statistical, xi, 15,
    170
Experiments, design of, 15-26
Explorer's problem, 40

183

184